Joe Cullen, aka 'Bard of Dalston', is a Liverpool-born poet and jobbing social scientist who has been living in the East End of London for the past twenty-odd years. His work has appeared in a range of poetry magazines and journals including 'South Poetry, 'South Bank Poetry', 'Other Poetry', 'Long Poem Magazine', 'Decanto', 'The North', 'Stand', 'The Delinquent', and 'Footballpoets.org'.

Poetry awards and commendations include: 'Poetry Pulse', 2012; 'Rhyme & Reason', 2012; 'Sportswriters Awards', 2012; 'Four Counties Poets', 2015. He has given poetry readings at Torriano, London; Royal Academy of Dramatic Arts (RADA), Salisbury Arts Centre, Barbican Arts Centre, the Crystal Palace Festival and the Kentish Town Festival. He was nominated for the Forward Prize, 2011. This is his first venture into the world of prose.

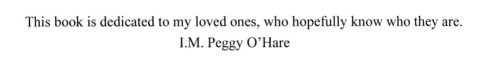

This book is dedicated to my loved ones, who hopefully know who they are.
I.M. Peggy O'Hare

Joe Cullen

COMING UNSTUCK—A YEAR IN THE LIFE OF A FAILED FUNK BAND

AUSTIN MACAULEY PUBLISHERS™

LONDON ∗ CAMBRIDGE ∗ NEW YORK ∗ SHARJAH

A CIP catalogue record for this title is available from the British Library.

ISBN 9781528984973 (Paperback)
ISBN 9781528987059 (Hardback)
ISBN 9781528987073 (ePub e-book)
ISBN 9781528987066 (Audiobook)

www.austinmacauley.com

First Published 2023
Austin Macauley Publishers Ltd®
1 Canada Square
Canary Wharf
London
E14 5AA

This book is blessed with a wealth of inputs and insights from other people, from whose great expertise and authority I have borrowed. Oliver Burkeman's regular column in *The Guardian*—'This column will change your life'—was a huge source of inspiration, as was his book *The Antidote: Happiness for people who can't stand positive thinking.*

The influencing academic sources are obvious—Richard Dawkins' *The Selfish Gene* and Susan Blackmore's *The Meme Machine* are key texts. The historical background on the Reivers comes from a number of sources, including Georg MacDonald Fraser's *The Steel Bonnets: Story of the Anglo-Scottish Border Reivers*; Keith Durham's *The Border Reivers: Men at Arms*; Michael Hornsby-Smith's *Catholics in England* and Alistair Moffat's *The Reivers: The Story of the Border Reivers.*

The history of Liverpool's often fraught dance with authority is supported by a number of texts, including John Smith's article in the *History Workshop Journal*, 1984 and the series of articles on Liverpool strikes provided by *catalystmedia.org.uk.* Every effort has been made in the book to quote citations from sources. A humble apology is offered for any citation omissions.

Table of Contents

Foreword

This book is a faction. A thing that lives somewhere between fact and fiction. A pastiche of happenings loosely clinging to the life belt of reality. Although based on actual events, these events are depicted through the perspective of the narrator—in particular, the grotesquely caricatured descriptions of the band.

Prologue

Ladies and Gentlemen.

Let me introduce you to the band.

On drums—all the way from East Finchley, via Cape Cod, it's the Prince of the Hi-Hats, the Titan of Toms, the Sultan of Snare—Mr Cyrus Dactyl!

On bass guitar—dig those deep-down dirty tones—give it up for oedipally-challenged posh boy—Mr Brendan Bazzle!

On rhythm guitar, coaxing the love from those worn-out frets, it's the rottweiler of rock—Pete Dankpatch!

Caressing the ivories, on keyboards, the incomparable, irreplaceable Mr Duff Jones!

On horn let's hear it for that sultry seducer of the saxophone, Mr Max Beauregard!

Belting out the backing vocals, put your hands together for the Queen of the Scream—Miss Flimsy Wipers!

And last but not least, on lead vocals, it's yours truly—numero uno, Il Duce. The Guv'nor.

January

"I'LLL—FFF—UUU—CCC—KKK—INN—GGG—KIII—LLL YOU."

I'm being chased around a rehearsal studio in Hackney Road by a six-foot twenty-stone drummer from West Africa. He's waving a Paiste Ride cymbal above his head with intent. Twenty-two centimetres of bronze, cut to a leading edge. Into my mind slips that scene from Goldfinger when Oddjob separates a statue's head clean from its torso after Bond has collected his golf winnings from a peeved Auric outside the clubhouse.

Luckily, I have an advantage. Cyrus has a potent stammer. He makes the mistake of shouting out insults as he pursues me. But the insults slow him down. Eventually, we both grind to a halt. Slide down the sweaty walls of the studio. The band looks on impassively.

Cyrus is a Jesus freak. He's forever writing songs about Jesus—what Jesus has for breakfast; what Jesus buys when he goes to Marks and Spencer; what Jesus thinks about a six-eight time signature. Because Cyrus is a big presence, the band has agreed to include some of his songs in its set-list. This wasn't formally sanctioned at a band meeting. We didn't put it to a vote. It was a survival mechanism.

The problem is Cyrus had begun to realise the band takes the piss out of his Jesus songs. It's not that the music's bad—he's got a good sense of rhythm and the beats are infectious. The problem is the lyrics. There's one song about people praying in churches. It's so twee the band have developed strategies to distance itself from it. At gigs, when it's played, we wink knowingly at the audience. One way of winking is to ironically bellow out the chorus at the top of our voices. Another way is to substitute obscenities for the God-words. Example:

Cyrus lyric: The people in the churches pray, ay-ay-yah.

Band substitute lyric: The people in the churches wank, ay-ay-yah.

Normally, Cyrus has no idea his God-lyrics are being bastardised by heathens who as sure as hell will end up in hell. This is because the stage configuration positions Cyrus at the rear of the band.

Duff, the keyboard player, is to his right about ten degrees to the front. Brendan, the bass player, is to his left about ten degrees to the front. Max, the sax player, is about thirty degrees to the side. The lead guitarist is on the same latitude as Max. Flimsy, the backing singer, is cavorting all over the place, but still in front of Cyrus and I'm occupying position numero uno, at the front of the grid—the tip of the diamond—the lead singer.

In this configuration, Cyrus doesn't have a clue what's being sung. The front stage monitors have the power of a couple of superannuated moths flapping their way around a bathroom light towards oblivion. So, Cyrus hears sound through the audience's reaction.

The thing is, in the last couple of gigs, audience reaction to the Praying song had been a spasm of collective laughter as Duff and I did exaggerated masturbation hand gestures in time with the chorus. He knows something is up. So, at the start of rehearsal, Cyrus pokes the elephant into the room and asks if there's a problem with his songs. The band shuffles uncomfortably. Looks down at its collective feet. Collaboratively nudges me as its putative leader. I clear my throat.

"Well, it's like this, Cyrus," I murmur, avoiding his eye. "'Pray for you' is a nice song but we're not sure it's what the punters in Dingwalls want to hear on a Saturday night."

"What do you mean?" says Cyrus, folding tree-trunk arms as he leans back perilously on the tiny drum stool.

"Well, the thing is—they're all pissed. But they're not so pissed, they can't understand the lyrics."

"What's wrong with the lyrics?" says Cyrus as he begins to tap out a threatening tattoo on the side of his snare drum.

I look around at the band for support but they're all looking the other way. I try to phrase my response delicately but it doesn't come out right.

"Well, to be honest, Cyrus. It's embarrassing. We're singing this shit about people praying—and the audience—they're all having a laugh."

The increased rapping of the drumstick on the rim of the snare signals Cyrus's increasing irritation. It's like mercury climbing the thermometer or that rapid reddening of neck when an allergic bites into a tuna steak. And when Cyrus gets annoyed, the stutter kicks in. My big mistake was to catch Duff's eye and do a quick masturbatory hand gesture when I thought Cyrus wasn't looking. But he was. Cue the farcical chase around the studio.

When we've regained our breath, a band discussion follows. Cyrus kicks it off.

"But what about your D—aaaa—ddd Song," he shouts, stabbing an accusing finger in my direction.

I hate to admit it but the Dad Song was probably a bridge too far. I'd introduced it at the previous rehearsal, with the intention of adding a bit more spice to a set list that had begun to feel too tepid. The set-list is what makes the band heroes or muppets. Get it right and you gradually crank up the audience to the point where—in the finale when you introduce the band—the goodwill in the room is so glutinous you could surf on it. Get it wrong and they throw bottles at you long before you've got to the finale.

The set-list is all about choreography. We start with an instrumental. It's like the warm-up to a gym session. The band gets to flex its musical muscles. The lead singer gets to stalk the stage, looking charismatic. The opener is designed to lull the audience into a false sense of ownership. Then we take over. The rest of the set is designed like a big dipper. You do a couple of ballads. Then you up the tempo. Then you do a storming number that takes them to the precipice. Then the interval kicks in. Then you start it all over again.

I wrote the Dad Song to surf us through to the interval. It takes the audience to the precipice. To understand it—Ladies and Gentlemen—let me introduce to you, my Father. The one and only Scouse Caruso. Give it up for *Sinbad the Sailor*. The teenage Balladeer who tours cities and shires on the under-card supporting Stefan Grappelli and Django Rheinhart—those legendary pioneers of Quintette Gypsy Jazz.

My dad's only sixteen and already he's singing tear-jerkers like Danny Boy and Rose of Tralee to packed houses at the Croydon Hippodrome and the Kilburn Empire. My dad was a top tenor. So good he'd been offered an apprenticeship at La Scala in Milan. But his own dad—my grand-dad—decided he didn't want his son cavorting with a bunch of Nancy Wops and slapped a veto on the apprenticeship.

So, my dad went off to sea. Whatever country you cared to name, he'd been there. Banana boats to Costa Rica. Oil tankers to the Middle East. Container ships to Australia. We wouldn't see him from one year to the next. I was probably just short of a year when he first clapped eyes on me. He turned up on Christmas Eve, staggering up the road after a diversion to Yates' Wine Lodge. When I saw him, I burst into tears—the start of a long and confrontational relationship in which each increasingly thought the other a total twat.

But over the years, when he was home I spent hours absorbing his favourite musicals—South Pacific, Oklahoma, Camelot, Porgy and Bess—cranked out from an old Decca gramophone in the front room as his own voice—far better than the famed recording artists who featured on the records and sung at top volume over the soundtrack—eclipsed them all. One time at school I found myself singing, "I'm gonna wash that man right out of my hair" out loud as a crowd of spotty woolly-backs gathered menacingly around me.

The woolly-back thing was the top item on a long list of things I hated him for. His unforgivable—and unforgiven—sin was to sanction a move that exiled us from Liverpool to that woebegone fly-trap they call Greater Manchester. And taking me out of Liverpool contributed to the second top item on the list of things I hated him for. Taking me out of Liverpool took me out of Liverpool School of Music—at whose hallowed halls I'd managed to get a place.

In my more paranoid moments, I'd convinced myself he'd sanctioned the move to woolly-back land because he was jealous. Taking me out of music school, I reasoned, was part of a cunning plan to tourniquet my musical development so I'd never reach a stage of competence that would threaten his. There was plenty of evidence to support this hypothesis.

When he was home, the green-eyed monster followed him around like a ship's dog. He'd compete incessantly, vying with his offspring for our mother's attention, shamelessly cheating at Monopoly.

I remember Christmas nineteen-sixty-five. The mistletoe already shrunk, the pine needles on the tree dropped like flies. And Sinbad arrives from somewhere—no clue, maybe Timbuktu—my aul fella, my dad. He's bevved as a skunk and in an alcohol-fuelled bad mood. Staggers into the house clutching a bunch of badly-wrapped Christmas presents. As he comes into the living room, he trips over a discarded toy and the presents fall from his arms like dead stars and tumble to rest on the chimney breast.

He stoops to pick them up. Can't be fucked. Leaves them to burn. Turns to the fruits of his sperm lined up like mascots in the living room. Next day, for no particular reason, he lands me a clout, then apologises. Says it doesn't mean nowt and ruffles my cow-curl. Takes me to Anfield for the big game. Leaves me perched on a stool with a milk-shake outside the Star and Garter while he's inside supping porter.

But when that Blue Funnel steamer chugged through the Albert Dock with him on it and disappeared from view past New Brighton, so did his interest in us. From the moment of his departure—hoisting his canvas carry-all onto those huge shoulders—to the sound of his return—footsteps tapping unsteadily down the road like Blind Pugh—we heard nothing but silence.

As we waited, milestones flitted by. The transition from nappies to the pot. From pot to toilet. First Holy Communion. School debut. Parents' Evenings. The shocking appearance of pubic hair. Weddings. Funerals. Anniversaries. All punctuated by the absence of his presence. My mother would write birthday cards on his behalf, artlessly signing them 'from Dad' in her own unmistakeably neat calligraphy.

And into that void stepped Mrs Murphy, Music Teacher. The grand irony is—it was the music teacher's fault I never learned to play the piano. From an early age, Mrs Murphy detected germs of musical talent in my rebellious demeanour. She persuaded me to stay behind after class to work on my vocal technique. She polished my scales. Arranged private lessons to accelerate my scansion. Enrolled me in cringe-making music competitions.

I remember one where I found myself on stage at the Adelphi Theatre—the same venue my dad had played years before—crimson-faced and dressed in a too-tight yellow and black striped pullover my mum had bought on the Provident that made me look like a fat wasp—singing 'On Wings of Song Far Sailing' as shame washed over me like toilet cleaner.

Mrs Murphy applied—successfully—on my behalf to the Liverpool School of Music. But even while she was laying the foundations of my musical development, she was laying the foundations of a broader philanthropic agenda. How to elevate a bunch of Toxteth scallies to the sunlit uplands of conspicuous consumption. Successive parents' evenings with my mother had convinced her you needed to take the Scouser out of Liverpool to take Liverpool out of the Scouser.

So, she inserted the germ of social mobility into my mother's oven-ready head. The kids would never make it if we stayed put. They'd grow up thick and feral. They'd amount to nothing. They'd sell drugs or their bodies or both. The best thing a mother could do if she wanted a future for her children would be to take them out of the Dockland slime-pits and build a new life in a nice, leafy environment. The germ put its feet up. Suckled lazily on my mother's infinite reservoirs of maternal love. Grew fat and demanding. Then burst out.

And so it was we arrived on the edge of a slag-heap near Wigan. Shipped out from a prefab in Kirkby to a semi-detached on a new estate not far from an old disused colliery. It might as well have been to an out-world settlement on the rings of Saturn.

In Liverpool, we called the inhabitants of these grim former mining towns woolly-backs, on account of their alleged habitual coupling with sheep. There was no love lost. I transitioned from a scally comprehensive to a woolly-back grammar school ruled with an iron hand by a bunch of cassock-wearers called the Christian Brothers. Christian in name. Not in nature.

There was one particular Brother called Brother Benedict. His party trick was to steal up behind you with a hefty wooden blackboard eraser and whack you over the head with it until you were close to unconsciousness. Then there was the paedo-priest—Father O'Dirty—who, under the pretext of swimming lessons, would get us to hold him up horizontally in the shallow end of the municipal pool while he demonstrated the crawl technique, all the while threshing like a Mississippi steamboat as he brought your hand inexorably closer to his crotch.

The upshot is, in the absence of the classical training I would have enjoyed had I taken up my place at Liverpool School of Music, I can't really play a note. I can do Chopsticks on the piano and a pared down version of Duelling Banjos on a string guitar. But that's as far as it goes. I write songs in my head. That's the easy bit.

Then comes the painful process of transcribing the technicolour glory of the song in my head into single strokes on a Yamaha keyboard. Plink plonk. Then remembering how it sounds and writing it down on manuscript paper with the notes in my head transposed into musical staves. I used to fantasise about having a USB port inserted into the side of my skull so the song that was inside my head could be downloaded straight to a four track. I guess I could have turned up at the rehearsal studio and hummed the tune but it's not a good look for the frontman.

So, I wrote this song on the Yamaha about my father. It's called—'My dad was a Cunt'. It's in 4/4 time and written in the key of G minor with a verse-verse-chorus-verse-chorus structure. Here's the lyrics:

There's no way to express this
in delicate language
thoughts that rear up
when I take a shower
when I haul out the garbage
I think them when I eat
a saucisson sandwich
it's always the same message
my dad was a cunt

There's no way to express the dread
of invites to classmates' houses
I turn up at their door
with a bunch of cellophane flowers
when it opens I'm confronted
by kids and pets and beautiful spouses
I'm completely astounded
my dad was a cunt

My dad was a cunt
there's no way to tell it but blunt
he turns up at Christmas
with a packet of biscuits
my dad was a cunt

There's no way to express the incision
of a visit to Pentonville Prison
the dart in your heart
when your world falls apart
my dad was a cunt.

My dad was a cunt
there's no way to tell it but blunt
he turns up at Christmas
with a packet of biscuits
my dad was a cunt

I think it's a great track but when I distribute the song sheet at rehearsal, there's an uncomfortable silence, followed by a series of technical questions like what's the tempo and where does the saxophone come in. I can't escape the impression they're dissembling—that the band's heart is not in it. But as Talleyrand said, politics is the systematic cultivation of hatred so I plough on. At the end of the night, we've licked the track into shape and I'm confident the band owns 'My dad was a Cunt'.

Until now.

Cyrus goes back to tapping the snare drum.

"What about the Dad Song?" he says.

I detect a subtle shift in collective allegiance, the sense of losing the dressing room. Duff looks down at his sneakers. Flimsy is studying her nail appendages. Then draws herself to her full pygmy height and expresses her opinion.

"It's not a nice song. My own dad wouldn't like it. And he's not a cunt."

Max—who's intent on getting into her knickers and will take any opportunity to ingratiate himself—takes the opportunity.

"I think Flimsy's right," he says. "It's not our style."

Pete, the rhythm guitarist, who for years has been shouldering the monkey of being sacked by Shire Draits just before they got famous is only too happy to jump on the bandwagon.

"It's a shit song. We're a jazz-funk band, not the fucking Pistols. I vote we ditch it."

Brendan takes his usual techno-diplomatic tack, pointing out the clunky key change between the verse and chorus. But there's already four votes clocked up against. A majority. No point arguing the toss. Bow out gracefully and store up the slight for later. Revenge is a dish best served on the red-hot coals of Wembley Arena at a point in the not-too-distant future.

The band don't seem to understand they need to take risks to succeed. The music business is a hierarchical ecosystem. It's built on layers. At the bottom are poor deluded individuals tapping out tunes in their bedrooms. At the top are record company A-listers. In the middle are bands like us grafting hard in venues no-one at the top would be seen dead in, trying to cross that bridge between amateur and professional.

The thing is, there's no objective test for professionals. The professionals don't pass exams, like architects or lawyers. They stay amateurs until someone says they're professionals. That someone is the promoter.

There's two promoters who control the ecosystem in London. Let's call them Bill and Ben but not to their face, them being ex-boxers. They made a tidy pile out of boxing. But they had the good sense to get off the treadmill before their brains got bashed out. They've put a lot of their pile into live music promotion. I'm always Open House to Bill and Ben. I have their phone number tattooed on my bicep. When they call, I jump.

The way it works with Bill and Ben is that they get you a gig at a well-known venue. The most well-known is the Rock Garden in Covent Garden—right opposite the Royal Opera House. The Rock Garden is a honey trap for tourists weaving their way from the pubs and bars in Leicester Square looking for something else to do after they've sunk a few pints and a couple of Jägermeister chasers. So it's always mobbed with half-pissed Romford chancers and trouser-creased ingenues off the tour bus from Beijing.

You'd think it would be a band goldmine. But you'd be wrong. How it works is Bill and Ben print the tickets for your gig. You're responsible for getting the audience to the venue. You get a small percentage of the revenue from the tickets you sell. You don't get any percentage of the footfall that staggers into the venue off the streets. Which is usually seventy per cent of the audience.

Bill and Ben are uber-capitalists. They understood from day one that music is a commodity like any other commodity. They've never allowed sentiment to get in the way of profit. That's why even on a good day a band can sell a hundred tickets but still make a loss because of the gig expenses.

I got a call from Ben a few days after the dad incident in the rehearsal studio. He's promoting a gig at the Water Rats. Kings Cross. The headline band have cancelled at short notice. Can we fill-in? I tell him I'll check out the band's availability.

I call Cyrus. No answer. I call Brendan. He tells me he's babysitting. I call Flimsy. As usual, she's up for anything. I call Pete. He doesn't like the venue. Looks like there's no way we'll fill the bill. I'll need to soft-soap Ben. I call him up expecting a load of grief—but he's cool. Tells me he's already got a replacement. Some band from Manchester. Lots of local punters coming down in coaches to support them. Lots of potential lolly. Call themselves Oasis. Can't help thinking it's a muppet name. There's no palm trees in Old Trafford. No desert unless you count Maine Road. But—result—crisis averted.

A band is what happens when you realise you're stuck. It started with the ashram. I was sitting in a pub in East London. It smells of cheap disinfectant and warmed pies. The pub is busy, even at this late hour on a Sunday evening. Peru versus Ecuador stutters on a giant TV screen. A St Joseph's hospice collecting tin, chained to a Fosters' lager pump, leans drunkenly over the bar.

Around the bar, a dozen identical stools, each upholstered in the same faded ox-blood as the ceiling, prop up a dozen identical drinkers, their faces as leached as the threadbare carpet that covers the floor. A large faux-gilt mirror fixed to the anterior wall returns their stares.

At the table below, two solitary women drink Pina Collada and pluck pork scratchings from a chipped saucer. A jukebox rumbles monotonously, piping out a Johnny Cash monologue. A statue of Charlie Chaplin, hands in pockets and shirt front flapping, casts a disconsolate eye over the bar as two young Goths tongue each other furiously. A forlorn heart-shaped balloon, with the words 'My Valentine', faded but still visible at its centre, dangles listlessly above them.

It's 11:30 PM and I've been here for hours, trying to think of a good idea to change my life. Become notorious. But I'm stuck for ideas. Stuck for thoughts. Stuck for words. I'm in a place that's licensed for stuckness. Everyone here is stuck. Sinking my fourth pint of the evening, I start to think about why I'm in a trap. Since I was a kid, I always wanted Fame. Yet, I always found diversions to avoid the effort needed to become Famed. Football. Going out. Passing examinations. Doing dissertations. Doing drugs. Doing nothing. As John Lennon said—Life is what happens to you while you're busy making plans.

I started to think about why it was always easier to choose the diversion than the action. I thought about how my mind works. What motivates me. What I was afraid of. I thought about what shapes my motivations and fears. I thought about how much control I thought I had to change things and how much I actually had.

I thought about other people I knew who talked about moving to an ashram or growing organic vegetables or writing a block-buster or starting a rock and roll band but who stayed in the same old routine. I thought about the millions of people I didn't know who were in much worse situations than me. People who were born in the wrong place at the wrong time.

I thought that people see life as so beyond their competence, so out of their control, that they become the rabbit frozen in the headlights. Or people feel so trapped and cornered by circumstance and inadequacy they see no way out. Then they do something crazy. Like Travis Bickel, in Taxi Driver, they declare their own personal war on their sense of powerlessness.

On 7 October 2008, a twenty-nine-year-old man holds forty-two call centre staff hostage on the fifth floor of a building in Guatemala City. He opens fire on three paramedics who tried to enter the building to talk to him. He claims to have an explosive device and shoots and wounds a security guard before threatening to blow up the building.

Police says the hostage-taker, Luis Fernando Escobar, had a 'sentimental' problem and had demanded to see his former girlfriend and her new boyfriend, who both worked at the call centre Escobar worked at. Escobar didn't have any specific demands but kept asking for a pastor. When the minister arrived, he broke down and released the hostages.

Escobar's futile attempt to resolve the unresolvable is a study in stuckness. Luis is trapped in the ghost of a relationship. We can speculate that his former girlfriend felt trapped in her relationship with Luis and felt compelled to find someone else. Luis is devastated. He tries to get her back. He sends hourly texts to her mobile. He sends flowers round to her mother's house. He tries pleading. He tries flattery. He tries bribery. None of this works.

He spends hours in Zona Viva bars, drinking grimly. He gets morose and angry. He tries textual abuse, stabbing terse, inadequate SMSs into his mobile phone. He leaves tearful, incoherent and threatening messages on his ex-girlfriend's voicemail.

As a last resort, he turns for salvation to violence and to God. All Luis succeeded in doing was to reinforce the cycle of stuckness that had got him into his situation in the first place. He had no plan to get himself out of this cycle. When it became evident that he wasn't going to succeed in re-writing history, Luis abdicated all responsibility for his own actions and placed his destiny in the hands of a higher power.

It's the same when you buy a lottery ticket. The odds of winning the jackpot are approximately one in fourteen million, yet people still buy tickets. They place their destiny in the hands of another higher power—fate. The lottery represents the paradox of stuckness. On the surface, winning the lottery presents the perfect way out of a dead-end. Yet, actually winning the lottery generates choices that create fear and loathing.

According to one survey, one in three who win big on the Lottery carry on working. Take Luke Pittard—the Lottery winner so bored of life on easy street he got his old job back at McDonald's. Or Callie Rogers, who gave up her supermarket job after winning £2 million but was back at work a fortnight later—

earning £4.85 an hour—after a diet of daytime TV soap became too much. Or Germany's biggest individual lottery winner who reported the Daily Mirror, had no time to celebrate after becoming 27 million dollars richer—because he was too worried about being late for work.

The Lottery offers an ideal form of escapism from stuckness. It's cheaper than the movies and you don't have to sit in a movie theatre for a couple of hours. People don't really expect to win—but they like to fantasise about the numbers rolling their way. More importantly, subconsciously, people don't actually want to win. Why? Because it challenges their conditioning.

Conditioning is what makes us stuck. Conditioning is living in a housing sink in the inner city instead of moving to a garden suburb. It's staying with the wrong partner when you should have split up years ago. It's dialling pensioners from a call centre in Milton Keynes to sell them health insurance. It's sparking up a cigarette when you've just learned your father is dying from lung cancer.

The opposite of being stuck involves making choices. It's choosing to move from a garden suburb to live in a housing sink in the inner city. It's celebrating the thirty years you and your partner have been together by doing a synchronised bungee jump off Victoria Falls. It's understanding how Big Tobacco operates and becoming an anti-tobacco activist.

One book I read defined stuckness as 'a self-perpetuating cycle of repetitive behaviour that prevents the possibility of change'. It's comfortable to think that only certain people get stuck. Thickies. People who have no vision or perspective. Yet, this simply isn't true. Stuckness is how the ruling elite keeps us ruled.

The Middle East's 'peace process'—an endless series of failed initiatives going nowhere—the 1946 Anglo-American Commission plan; the 1947 UN General Assembly Resolution 181; the 1978 Camp David framework; the second Camp David framework in 2000; the Quartet Road Map of 2002; the Arab Peace Initiative of 2007. All totally ineffectual.

Climate change. In 1896, a Swedish chemist, Svante Arrhenius, produces a model that could calculate the rate of global warming from human-created CO_2 emissions. 1938—British researcher Guy Callender produces the first empirical evidence of an association between global warming and levels of carbon dioxide. 1971—the SMIC conference in Stockholm issues stern warnings about the risk of severe climate change.

1997—the Kyoto Conference on Climate Change is indelibly associated with polarised positions and political in-fighting. The subsequent Kyoto Protocol is fatally compromised. Half the population don't believe the evidence on global warming and politicians do nothing. These things are illustrations of a collective failure of nerve. Our so-called leaders continually reinforce the status quo. Stuckness is built into the systems constructed to regulate us.

The psychologist and newspaper column-writer Oliver Burkeman has a good handle on stuckness. I read one of his articles that quoted Po Bronson, author of *What Should I Do With My Life?*, a book about people who made major life changes. Bronson writes the book at a time when he had hit a point in his own life when he 'wanted to know where he was headed'.

He reasons that everyone aspires to compose a narrative of their own life that is seen by others as meaningful. Bronson travels the USA looking for these narratives. He maps nine hundred personal experiences of people who set out to try to answer the age-old question: 'who am I and where am I going?' and whittles these down into fifty stories.

The protagonists are a diverse bunch: rich and poor; young and old; religious and heretical. What binds them together is their search for transformation or as Bronson puts it, their willingness to try to unearth their 'true calling'. Not many of them succeeded. Most were still in their jobs long after they'd planned to make a new life. They had ended up so psychologically conditioned to their world that changing it became a fantasy.

Burkeman says this tendency to cling on to grim reality whilst fantasising about possible futures is ingrained in humans. He cites Rolf Potts' book on serial travelling *Vagabonding*, as a good illustration of how people constantly dream about packing in their jobs so they can travel around the world. The book highlights people who are like the character played by Charlie Sheen in the film *Wall Street*.

This character justifies his workaholic lifestyle on the grounds that if he makes enough cash by his thirtieth birthday he will be able to ride his motorcycle across China. As Potts points out, "You could work for eight months as a toilet cleaner and have enough money to ride a motorcycle across China."

The real issue is not about the futility of escapism. As Burkeman says, it's about "our tendency to inflate the resources we think we'd need to pursue our dreams. If you can convince yourself you can't afford to do something, you're spared having to take the anxiety-provoking actions that might turn it into reality."

Under the watchful gaze of Charlie Chaplin, in a downbeat pub in London's East End, as I started to think about why I couldn't get started on becoming notorious, I began to realise there was a fundamental psychological block I was struggling with.

But I also began to realise it wasn't just about my personality. It was also about my family, my background, my culture and my history. It was about the control systems that squeeze the life out of our creativity. It was about stuckness. That's when I decided to check out ashrams. I reasoned that to think out of the box you need to get out of the box. Exchange Charlie Chaplin for a yurt in the Himalayas.

My dad calls me. He's never called me in his life. There's a couple of minutes of embarrassing foreplay as we skirt around the reason he's called me. He asks how the girls are. He's always shown more interest in my daughters than he's shown interest in his own offspring. We finally cut to the chase. He's got a job with an engineering crew replacing the boilers that heat the Houses of Parliament. He wants to come down and stay with me while he does the job. He's got his own security pass. I accept his invitation. It's the first time in over twenty years I'll be living with my dad.

I give him explicit instructions about how to get down to London and where to meet. He's travelling in a minivan with a bunch of dodgy Scouse builders and engineers who have probably scammed the contract because they have compromising photographs of their MP stretched out unconscious on a triple king-size bed in one of those new hotels off the Pier Head.

The instructions predictably go pear-shaped. He's not at the house when I turn up. I endure an hour of waiting before my phone rings. It's a number I don't recognise. But it's him. He's in the Trolley Stop down the road. He's mislaid the instructions and got lost. He doesn't have a mobile phone but a really kind bloke in the pub has loaned him his own mobile and he's only charged him ten quid for the call. I go down to the Trolley Stop determined to punch the living daylights out of the Cockney twat who's conned my dad but it's too late. The twat has disappeared along with the tenner he's conned.

At the same time as I want to avenge my conned dad, my inner vindictive child wants to take this opportunity to revel in his being conned. My inner vindictive child instinctively sees its chance to turn the tables on the past when it felt powerless in the face of those Popeye forearms. I remembered all those times after he'd hoisted his bag onto those huge shoulders and disappeared down the Dock Road when my mother was called upon to staunch my deep sense of loss. She'd come up with me to my bedroom and read me stories to soothe me until she thought I was asleep.

After she'd switched off the lamp, I'd pull up the flannelette and tie the corners to the bedposts. I'd pretend I was under canvas and open the Atlas she'd given me for my birthday, turn to the page where the Atlantic spreads itself like an albatross and in the amber torchlight, I'd trace the latitude from home to where the ocean ended. Run a fingernail from Liverpool all the way to Boston.

Then I'd close my eyes, soar across the great divide, steer so close to the swell I'd feel spray on skin. My radar navigated whirlpools until I arrived on his ship. I'd slip over the rail, quietly pad the deck to the mess room and peer through the port-hole. But then I'd seen his shadow engulfing an old mahogany desk, a glass of rum crushed in that Meccano fist. And as I gazed I'd hear the swish of waves kiss pebbles on New Brighton Beach. Feel the gathering gloom that would bring home the storm.

I get to the Trolley Stop. My dad there propped up against the bar, desperately seeking the familiar—head spinning like a weather-cock in a gale. And he sees me and breaks into this huge grin. And my vindictive child gets conned. He doesn't hug me. That would be too intimate—too profound. But all those past torments—the absences, the forgotten birthdays, the holidays that never happened, the slashes of gratuitous violence—seem to dissolve into that grin as he buys me an ale. And another. And although our intercourse is mainly silence punctuated by stabs of conversation, we stay far too long.

Making our way back home we cross Culture Square. I see a man walking with a pizza slice held chest-high like an offering. He's chewing a corner of quattro staggioni while murmuring into some kind of device. Above his head, I see an orchestra of angels abseiling from a cloud attesting to the miracle of me and my Father. In step. Together.

The angels hover an inch above his head the beat of air fanned by their wings gently ruffling his hair as they sing acapella. But my dad is oblivious. I alone see the miracle and we continue our way my dad and I breast-stroking through the pressure waves of Kingsland Road. We stop at the Ali Baba. Pick up a doner. My Father needs to be persuaded.

Although over many years he'd come back from sea bringing exotic recipes he'd transplant to the kitchen at home they were all bastardised versions of the vernacular. Chicken curry with boiled egg and tinned pineapples. He's not accustomed to kebabs. But I convince him to take one home. We eat in silence. Just like old times. In the gathering gloom.

February

The Manager has booked us a gig at the Hen and Chickens. It's one of those multi-tasking venues that shape-shifts to cater for different shades of grey. The Hen bills itself as a 'Theatre-Bar', combining drama, comedy, cinema and a space for artists to come together and find their voice. But its bread and butter is serving booze. That's why—particularly at the weekend—the coming together artists find themselves at the mercy of a pissed-up crowd.

I've never really liked the Hen. It's situated at the point where the A1, having made its journey all the way from Edinburgh, arrives exhausted at Highbury Corner. If you're in a vehicle, you have to negotiate a hostile roundabout. If you're not careful, the roundabout spits you out east to Dalston. If you're really unlucky, it shunts you back north to Edinburgh.

You couldn't make this up but the Hen's closest competitor is The Cock—a pub directly opposite, adjacent to Highbury and Islington Underground station. The Cock's main clients are those poor benighted bastards immortalised in Nick Hornby's novel *Fever Pitch*—Arsenal fans miserably shuffling their way to Highbury Stadium. Sometimes, the Cock and the Hen converge, usually on a Saturday night as Arsenal fans shuffle miserably back from the Stadium, looking for something to numb the pain of a tedious one-nil victory.

The main thing that makes me disinclined to like the Hen is that it doesn't have a stage. A stage is crucial to a band's sense of purpose. The stage is the point of separation between performer and crowd. If you don't have a stage you're the same as the audience. If you're the same as the audience, you're no longer an artist.

Without that performer-crowd separation, the fragile artifice of art is destroyed. A stage helps the band dominate the audience. Even at the height of a couple of feet, the audience is literally forced to look up to you. You look down on them. That's the perfect interpersonal relationship for a band. Totally asymmetrical.

In the absence of a stage, we're eye-level with the audience and that means we have to work much harder to maintain the fiction that—as artists—we're superior to them. Audiences are like chihuahuas. They're small and yappy but mostly compliant. Until they turn on you. Chihuahuas all look the same. That's why they add accoutrements to themselves. Sleeve tattoos. Nose piercings. Bits of flesh hanging out. But they're still chihuahuas. That's why you need a stage.

To compensate for its lack of a stage, the Hen creates an artifice of separation by cordoning off an alcove of the pub that looks out onto Highbury Corner. It's a bit like a larger version of the bay window you get in a suburban semi-detached, but without the chintz curtains. The absence of chintz curtains doesn't cut much ice with the band when it arrives and is shown its bay window. Cyrus kicks off first.

"I can just about get the drum kit in. Where are you guys gonna set up?"

Recognising a hissy-fit in the making, The Manager intervenes. There's a blackboard above the bar that displays the Hen's dishes of the day—traditional fish and chips; artisan burger; vegetarian lasagne. The Manager's eagle eye has noticed two sticks of chalk sitting invitingly at the foot of the blackboard. She takes one of the sticks and maps out a grid pattern in the alcove, chalking out lines across the Hen's dusty floor. When she's finished, there's seven neat little chalk squares, each designated with the name of its owner.

"You couldn't swing a fucking cat," mutters Pete as he insinuates himself reluctantly into his designated square.

The rest of the band follow suit, squeezing themselves into their own squares. Duff points out his keyboard is twice the width of the average band member, with the possible exception of Cyrus. The Manager re-arranges the squares to accommodate the band's equipment. Flimsy and myself—the only ones without equipment—are the ones who lose out. We're left with squares the size of a postage stamp.

Eventually, the mutterings and grumblings subside, the equipment is set up and we're ready for the sound check. We always sound check to Cantaloupe—a classic Herbie Hancock jazz standard. Designed to prep the band. It's an instrumental, so it doesn't involve the vocalists.

The vocalist's contribution to the sound check is more of an afterthought—a few grunts into a microphone when the musicians have finished mangling Herbie. The sound check goes to plan. There's some minor niggles with the stage monitors—a couple of twelve-inch woofers and horns that struggle to make themselves heard—but we're up and running.

Tonight marks the debut of a new song I've written called 'Come to my Rescue'. What the band don't realise, because they're total philistines, is that the song rips off the musical structure Mozart used in Act IV of Marriage of Figaro where the Count pleads forgiveness—*Contessa perdono*!—and the Countess forgives him—*Più docile io sono.* Except, it's conceptually reversed and the song is actually a rant about not being forgiven.

Of course, it's all shamefully derivative of Queen's Bohemian Rhapsody—which was of course shamefully derivative of Mozart's Marriage of Figaro. No-one in the band gets it except, paradoxically, Flimsy, who, like a turbo-charged hyena sinks her teeth into its meaty vocal role, sensing an opportunity to outshine yours truly.

The song is G major with a structure that's not your standard three minute chart-topper. It starts with a 4X4 in ballad format. Then the tempo cranks up dramatically into a thumping house beat that's maintained to the end, through an eight line conflict duet, wherein the first verse I whine on about how mistreated I am and then Flimsy responds with a withering denunciation of patriarchy and male self-indulgence, to the finale that repeats the one-line chorus—'Come to my Rescue'—eight times. Here's how it goes.

Intro—keyboard. Grand piano effect. 4 bars. Then I come in.

Empty room, space calls out your name
Tried every permutation but it still works out the same
Another lonely night without you
Come to my rescue
Unopened letters, doesn't live here any more
Still catch my breath
When there's someone knocking on my door
So hard to forget you
Come to my rescue
The real thing come
and it's so hard to define
catch the moment before it slips away
bind it to yourself and make it whole
before the disillusion strikes right at a heart

Failed expectations
Waves washing over me
Out of my depth
I'm drowning in a sea of troubles
throw me a lifeline
Come to my rescue

The last line repeats three times, ending on an up note that's sustained for four bars as Cyrus's bass drum drives a thumping change in tempo. The keyboard follows the up notes as the sax comes in mirrored by the rhythm guitar for eight bars taking us into Flimsy's response:

I hear you talking but the words all sound the same
Speak to me in another key
find someone else to take the blame
don't want to be your therapy
soothe your troubled mind
slave to your history looking back behind
(Come to my Rescue)
Rescue yourself
(Come to my Rescue)
I'm not a cure you can take down from the medicine shelf
I want to be your lover, not your mother
and it's so hard for you to discover
that my hands are tied

I follow with my own counter-response:

Your presence fills the frame of everything I do
Spend all my energy just trying to get over you
Try to convince myself I'm where I want to be
But I know I'm killing time and time is killing me
Take up arms in my defence
Fighting in opposition makes no sense
Being yourself is all so people say
but is it worth the price you have to pay.

Then the sax solo comes in for eight bars, leading into an eight-bar pause aimed at creating a suspense hook in the song—the guitars and keyboard anchoring the space repeating a simple three-note sequence until Flimsy and I harmonise the hook line repeated eight times *Come to my rescue* underscored by the entire band's instrumental accompaniment, building up to a perfectly synchronised endpoint *Come to.* I slip 'Come to My Rescue' midway into the second half of the set.

I'm apprehensive about how it will go down, considering it's not your average pub standard. To work, the song needs to hook the audience to the four balladic verses at the start, so we have them eating out of our hands as we crank up the beat and surf them through to the climax.

It's not looking good. I'm into the second verse, giving it my best Mario Lanza, but I'm picking up unmistakable signs of disinterest. Spontaneous conversations are breaking out. There's a steady trickle of punters to the bar. It gets worse. People are beginning to laugh. The kiss of death. They're nudging each other. Each nudge brings on a laugh. The laughter spreads mimetically through the crowd until the whole audience is laughing.

I plough on through the final fourth ballad verse, desperately hoping the transition to up-tempo will carry the crowd with us. And suddenly, the crowd go wild. They're cheering and stamping. Behind me, I can sense the band feeding off the crowd's energy. Their timing gets better. Their sound gets sharper. They're playing like a proper band. Tight. Coherent. Together. We storm through the finale, finishing on a dead stop that would make an Olympic figure skater envious. The crowd goes into ecstatic applause. A chant goes up. Rescue! Rescue!

The rest of the gig is almost an anti-climax. The band, energised by the reception to 'Rescue', deliver a storming sequence of numbers, finishing with an inspired version of 'Temple of Love' that would have got everyone on their feet if they hadn't already been on them. But we're all remembering how good 'Rescue' was.

Over a post-gig drink, we're basking in the afterglow of a Stadium-grade performance when one of the band's small group of regular fans joins us.

"Fantastic gig, guys," she says, as we make room for her to squeeze into the narrow alcove. I have a vague recollection she works for Hackney social services. She's wearing a denim jacket that's seen better days, so my recollection is probably accurate.

She lights up a cigarette and takes a gulp of her pint. Looks up and says, "Did you slip that bag lady a tenner to turn up?"

We all exchange blank looks.

"What bag lady?" says Duff.

She cracks up laughing and tells us what happened. I'm into the final ballad verse of 'Come to my Rescue'. The crowd are getting restless when out of nowhere a bag lady appears behind us at the alcove window. She's in full view of the audience, but the band have no idea she's there. She begins to sway slowly in time to the ballad. Then just as slowly she peels off her top.

The audience nudges each other. Start to laugh. The bag lady responds by swaying suggestively. The audience responds by cheering and clapping. The band is completely oblivious. We misinterpret the audience's behaviour as positive feedback. Cyrus cranks up the volume. Behind us the bag lady rubs her breasts against the window. She's popping and jiving. The audience roars. They're stamping up and down.

A chant goes up. Rescue! Rescue! The band feed off the audience. We all go wild. Brendan's vomiting riffs. Max farting diminuendos. Duff's banging keys. Flimsy and me, wailing. Then behind us in the plate glass window, a policeman's arm appears. Drags off the bag lady. The audience goes bananas. We mainline the applause.

Still, the bag lady did us a favour. 'Rescue' is now owned by the band. And the band now owns the Hen and Chickens. The management invites us back. That's a big plus on our gig card. The band are happy. The Manager is happy. The Manager takes me back to her house in suburban Outer London to add our happiness to the sum of happiness.

She's a volatile mix of geisha and dominatrix. She's got two kids—one a sulking volcano of pre-adolescent female angst—the other a lovely but shy boy already running to fat. Her life since her partner fucked off back to East Asia is attenuated chaos—crushed cornflakes on the kitchen floor—herding the kids out to the door for school—late—always late—cramming them into the Vestra turning the key the engine coughing spluttering then dying then coughing and spluttering and dying again—late—always late.

On this particular night, they're being looked after by their grandparents. The Manager has a thing about stretch marks. She's gone through three conceptions and two births if you count the miscarriage. The legacy is the stretch marks. She thinks it's her punishment. She thinks they're repulsive. In her head, they look like the tripe you see on a butcher's slab. She's like a vampire. Only comes out at night.

There's a kind of mutually assured destruction in our verse as we negotiate the tricky minefields of sex, stretch marks, drugs, rock and roll and possible future parents evenings.

In the morning, we retract like gorged terrapin. I listen to rain flood groaning drains in the street below as panic sets in. What are we doing here? Is this the start of a John and Yoko? What happens if she asks if she can play tambourine on the band's next gig? Where will it all end?

"Hush," she says, as I turn to spraff an exit line. "There is karma in words." And she traces a fingernail along the scar where my appendix had been.

Ever since I was born my life had been on hold. My life. A Big Wheel of repeated behaviours and lessons unlearned. A catalogue of untaken opportunities. Did I come from a long line of procrastinators? People who resisted change and stayed stuck? Was I descended from the original Stuckists, way before Billy Childish and Charles Thomson? I needed to find out.

I went back in time to look for clues. In the fifteenth century, my ancestors were Border Reivers—thieves and cattle-rustlers who roamed the no man's land between England and Scotland. Outlaws. They dined out on lawlessness. The constant wars between England and Scotland gave the Reivers perfect cover to pillage and plunder.

After the Union of 1603, the newly formed state flexed its muscles and put the boot into these outlaws. Some of my ancestors were executed. Others shipped to Ireland. In exile, we nurtured dreams of revenge and repatriation. When the Civil War in England broke out, we sensed an opportunity and stole back to the Scottish Borders. We encountered prosperous villages and comfortable farmers; roads and bridges; fortified garrisons—and the Scottish Enlightenment. There was no room for Reivers. As the realisation sank in that everything had changed and pillaging had dried up, we chose exile once more.

But when we snuck back to Ireland there was no-one home. A small matter of *phytophthora infestans* had escaped our notice. Whilst my ancestors were skulking the borders of Scotland, looking for fresh opportunities for rustling cattle and waylaying citizens, around a million of their more law-abiding former compatriots, starved out of Ireland by the potato famine, were humping their meagre possessions across the decks of groaning hulks bound for Liverpool,

Boston and New York. We were in the wrong place at the wrong time. We were *always* in the wrong place at the wrong time.

I wondered whether this propensity for being stuck had become hard-wired in our DNA. What if my tribe had developed entrenched strategies for resisting change? We were always marooned in times and places that had moved on. Yet, we persevered in the old ways. It's not only your mum and dad who fuck you up. It's their mum and dad and theirs and so on down the line.

If you were to select one of my extended family at random; took a surgical saw and cut out a section of the medulla oblongata, just below the corpus callosum, you would probably find the word 'stuck' neatly circumscribed, like a stick of Blackpool rock. The thing is bad genes may not be just about physical attributes like your appearance and your health. It's true I inherited MPB and a pigeon chest. But it could equally be true that I inherited a tendency to swim against the tide. I was a prisoner of stuckness long before I was born.

I looked to Richard Dawkins for enlightenment. *The Selfish Gene* talked about 'gene-centred evolution'. It said humans are 'survival machines—robot vehicles blindly programmed to preserve the selfish molecules known as genes'. It said Darwin's principle of 'survival of the fittest' is really a special case of a more general law of 'survival of the stable'. Nature is populated by stable things—planets, rocks, salt crystals, atoms. Natural selection accepted stable forms and rejected unstable ones.

At that good old dawn of time water, carbon dioxide, ammonia and methane merged together to form a particular molecule called the 'Replicator'. This new molecule rapidly spread copies of itself within the soup, becoming the dominant molecule and creating the conditions for a new kind of stability.

The modern descendants of these early replicators are DNA molecules. They provide the instructions on how to make a 'survival machine' and they control the chemical processes in the body's cells that enable it to do that. Genes are like a set of architectural plans that give the survival machine the information it needs so it can do things to survive.

I was totally baffled by this. How could natural selection possibly build stuckness into evolution? Surely, the point of evolution is that it would force the Reivers to improve—to become more efficient and more effective in order to survive. And sure enough, natural selection is about organisms that successfully adapt to changes in the environment or acquire new defences to cope with new predators.

Species make measurements that calculate the match between the current state they live in and the desired state they want to live in. Humans have developed particularly sophisticated devices to do these calculations—consciousness, memory and learning. By using these devices, humans have gone from living in caves to travelling to the moon.

But I learn that although natural selection is all about change, it's also about stability. Genes themselves have no consciousness. They just are. Their purpose is to ensure their own survival in the future. Genes are inherently selfish and inherently stable in the sense that survival and replication are what they exist for. And since their survival depends on the efficiency of the 'survival machines' that host them and which they help to build, then it follows that the evolutionary behaviour of these survival machines will favour stability.

I found out that the thing that works for stability is called an 'evolutionary stable strategy'. An ESS is 'a pre-programmed behavioural policy which, if most members of the population adopt it, cannot be bettered by an alternative strategy'.

The biologist Maynard Smith came up with some boys-own names for the strategies organisms use to maximise their success. There's the 'Retaliator' strategy—adopting a behaviour that's dependent on the behaviour of an opponent. A Retaliator behaves like a hawk when attacked by a hawk and like a dove when met by a dove.

There's the 'Bully' strategy. The Bully behaves like a hawk until an opponent hits back—at which point the Bully retreats. A 'Prober-Retaliator' mostly behaves like a Retaliator, but occasionally experiments by probing how far the opponent is likely to escalate the contest. If the opponent doesn't fight back, the prober persists in behaving like a hawk. If the opponent does fight back, the prober reverts to the behaviour of a dove.

If you simulate these different strategies in a computer programme, the Retaliator strategy alone fits the bill as evolutionary stable. This is broadly what happens in real life. Animals calculate the pay-off between fighting, winning, losing, being injured, wasting time that could have been spent finding food or shagging and so on. The calculation usually tells the animal that fighting is not the best strategy. That's why you see so much posturing in nature—beach poseurs flexing their muscles; a road rage driver baring his teeth; handbags at pub closing time—rather than actual fighting.

Another kind of calculation is based on territorial gains and losses. Evolutionary contestants who already have their feet under the table—the residents—usually enjoy advantages over those who arrive at that location later—the intruders. Residents are familiar with the terrain and don't have to use any resources getting to a location. The organism that is always an intruder is always taking a 'paradoxical' ESS.

The ESS of 'intruder wins, resident retreats' is a paradoxical strategy because the intruder will always be stuck in a never-ending search for more conquests. This expends a significant amount of time and energy. And it's also fundamentally unstable since if intruders became dominant, 'residents' would ultimately cease to exist and intruders would end up with only intruders to fight. That's a no-win situation.

The winners in the evolutionary game are organisms that adopt stable survival strategies. Stability is everything in the replication game. That's why many species are territorial. And that's why many species have developed memory. Some species—insects, for example—have a collective memory of what has beaten them and in what circumstances. Other species remember individuals who have beaten them. In a group of chimpanzees, the 'alpha male' is recognised because subordinate males remember previously being battered by him.

I discovered that the point of 'evolutionary stable strategies' is to establish stable sets of genes that can't be invaded by any new gene. Minority candidates in the gene pool are automatically playing catch-up simply because they are minority candidates. As Dawkins says "most new genes that arise, either by mutation or re-assortment or immigration are quickly penalised by natural selection: the evolutionary stable set is restored."

Things like having a good memory, occupying territory and maintaining a dominant hierarchy are all effective evolutionary stable strategies and they ultimately make the gene pool stable.

The memory of a past defeat at the claws of a large predator gets hard-wired into the DNA. But, more importantly, the *effect* of that defeat then becomes part of the gene pool. If a behaviour has a positive benefit for the organism (or vice versa), then it becomes part of the instructions the gene supplies to its survival machine to ensure the gene's survival in the future. Behaviour makes a bridge between the gene inside and the world outside.

The thing that lodged in my mind when I was working my way through The Selfish Gene is what Dawkins called 'phenotyping'—the 'bodily manifestation of a gene'. Genes not only influence how bodies improve their survival capabilities, there all also genes that influence how bodies make things outside their body.

These external constructions directly contribute to the body's—and hence the genes'—survival. The caddis fly is a brilliant phenotyper. It builds complex tubular houses out of old crap it picks up from the bed of a stream. Over time, through negative feedback, the caddis fly developed genes that tell the fly which crap will build the best house. This meant the fly got better at selecting the right crap for house-building from river beds. In turn, more effective crap-selection behaviour increased the chances of survival of the caddis fly gene pool.

As I started to think about my own gene pool, it began to dawn on me that the survival machines my ancestor genes built and the ESS's they adopted were really fucked up. It wasn't that they didn't promote stable sets of genes that couldn't be invaded by any new gene. That part of the ESS worked only too well. Indeed, no self-respecting invading gene would touch us with a barge pole. This was because we developed a gene for clannishness.

In the fourteenth and fifteenth centuries, the area where Scotland met England was a frontier environment in all senses. Despite the name, there was no 'Border' as such in the region where the Reivers lived; no clear demarcation or agreed territory. From 1296 onwards, when Edward I of England tried to take over control of Scotland, the two kingdoms were constantly at war—especially at the point where their two territories converged. There, it was all raping and pillaging and it allowed the Reivers to thrive.

The meaning of the word 'reiving'—plundering or raiding—says it all. 'Bereaved' in English is directly derived from the dead the Reivers usually left behind after a raid. Cattle rustling, feuding, murder, arson and pillaging were not only accepted forms of behaviour, they were seen as the only means of livelihood. Why bother farming when your harvest was likely to be scorched and your cottages burnt down?

Two further factors reinforced this Reiver mentality. Firstly, the environment, with its mountains and moorlands, discouraged farming but was good for grazing. Secondly, there was the inheritance system of *gavelkind*, which divided land equally between all sons on the death of the family head. This meant you ended up with a parcel of land the size of a shredded wheat, which was difficult to support a family. So, the Reivers became guerrillas.

They developed nifty skills in horsemanship and warfare but were equally adept in the arts of murder, extortion, arson, thieving and kidnapping. Their allegiance was to family and clan, not to church, region or state.

I discovered that the reiving families had a particularly lairy tradition—when a male child was christened his right arm was excluded from the ritual so that, in later life, he was free to wound and kill without being morally bothered. Blood ties meant that territory always came second to clan allegiance. Families often straddled both Scotland and England. Scottish Reivers were just as likely to raid other Scots as to raid the English across the Border. But Scots and English reivers would routinely join forces to pillage either side of the Border.

I came across a project led by John Burn, head of the Institute of Human Genetics at Newcastle University, that collected blood samples from people now living in the Border region. The aim was to build a genetic picture of the Border Reivers. His direct ancestor was Geordie Burn, a notorious Reiver who, the night before he was hanged in 1596, is reported to have confessed that 'he had lain with above forty men's wives—and that he had killed seven Englishmen with his own hand, cruelly murdering them; that he had spent his whole time in whoring, drinking, stealing and taking deep revenge for slight offences'.

Geordie was a resistant intruder. Like all Reivers, he was kin through and through. Outsiders were not tolerated. They were there to be kidnapped, cuckolded and murdered. Though inter-breeding between families and clans was normal, the extended Reiver clan system was largely impervious to gene pools from the outside. In Geordie, we see an example of what extended phenotyping might look like if you dressed it up in a brigadine, put a longbow in its hand and mounted it on a horse.

It also struck me that the Reiver's life exhibited all the characteristics of Maynard Smith's 'paradoxical evolutionary survival strategy'. The Reiver was a 'hawk', with a predatory lifestyle, seeking out and pouncing on organisms that were not of the bloodline and who appeared weak. Equally, the Reiver adopted an 'intruder wins, resident retreats' strategy.

Reivers had no real territorial base. They roamed the frontier, with its shifting boundaries and fluctuating allegiances. The Reiver's economic existence was predicated on the 'raid'. Sometimes, raids involved no more than a few armed men in a quick moonlight dash to an isolated farm to rustle a sheep. But other raids were much more extensive—Kinmont Willie—William Armstrong—was another notorious Reiver whose trademark was the large scale raid, involving upwards of 300 men 'Kinmont's bairns'—targeting whole areas rather than individual farms or villages.

Armstrong became immortalised, in the 'Ballad of Kinmont Willie', for an act of defiance that encapsulates the glamour, rebelliousness and sheer fucked-upness of the Border Reivers.

In March 1596, a Truce Day was held in the Borders, so the Scots and English could meet to negotiate deals and treaties. The Scottish side was represented by Kinmont Willie Armstrong. As Willie was riding home to his tower at Morton Rigg, just north of Carlisle, a bunch of devious English snuck out and captured him. Kinmont Willie was taken to Carlisle in chains.

The Scots saw this as a right old provocation since it was carried out on the day everyone assumed they were immune from arrest. The official of the area, the Warden of the March, tried to rectify the situation diplomatically. But since Willie was a Top Dog in the Border Reivers, the English were determined to keep hold of him. The Warden of the area, the Duke of Buccleuch, put together a posse of members of the main clan families and rode across the Border to Carlisle Castle.

The majority of the posse created a diversion. The rest reached Willie's cell and liberated him. The English were humiliated by their castle being invaded by the Scots and Queen Elizabeth was not best pleased with Sir Thomas Scrope, the commander of the Castle for allowing the humiliation. North of the Border, James VI of Scotland was so terrified that Buccleugh had ruined his chances of succeeding Elizabeth on the throne of England that he ordered Buccleugh to hand himself over to the English.

Following a judicious wait to allow tempers to cool down, Buccleuch did pop down to London to make his peace with the Queen. Elizabeth is reputed to have said "With ten thousand such men, James VI could shake any throne in Europe."

March

March came in like a rattlesnake, to borrow Ian Fleming from Dr No. I'm schlepping up the A41 towards Mill Hill in the clapped-out Citroen. The heavens are dumping a toxic mix of sleet, rain and road sludge onto the windscreen. The Citroen's wipers struggle to cope.

I can just make out the road markings through the small triangle of glass they've managed to carve out. I need a transport upgrade. My kids refuse to get into the Citroen now on account of the social embarrassment—the decapitated wing-mirror, algae growing around the window frames, headlights held together with gaffer tape. I envision the not-too-distant future. A four litre Bentley with personalised number plates: STAR-1.

Heading for Brendan's gaff—or more precisely the gaff of Brendan's parents. Brendan Senior flogs Harrier jets to sheikhs. Hence the palatial pile in North London. The neighbours include oligarchs, football managers, rock stars. Visitors include Cabinet Ministers and, occasionally, the Big Boss. We go there sometimes to write songs and finesse chords. Brendan Senior hates us because we divert his son's attention from getting a proper job.

Luckily, he's not around too much on account of having to attend international arms fairs in despotic regimes. His mother is more indulgent. When we turn up at the gaff, parking next to the helicopter pad in the back garden, she always makes sure we're provided with tea and carrot cake.

This time, the band is congregating in Brendan's conservatory to discuss the planning of the EP that will lead us to stardom and that four litre Bentley. The plan is to produce a CD showcasing three of the band's best songs. On paper, this should be easy. In practice, it's harder than producing a COP climate conference communique. It begins encouragingly.

Brendan's mum appears, distributes tea and carrot cake then disappears. The communal act of eating and drinking momentarily brings us together. Then the skirmishes start. Cyrus wants to include the God Song in the EP. I catch Duff's eye and stifle the urge to make a surreptitious masturbatory gesture. Flimsy puts in a plea for 'Temple of Love'—the appalling soul pastiche I'd written as a sop for those punters who felt the need to get up and dance at our gigs.

Pete makes a pitch for 'Ordinary Madness'. Coincidentally, it features complex guitar arpeggios. Max wants to include 'Come to My Rescue', which happens to include a sustained sax solo. I'm strongly lobbying for The Dad Song. In my head I'm already holding the CD, turning it over to reveal the front cover, the title snarling out rebellion with its forty-eight point Haettenschweiler font leering above a photograph of the band togged out in bondage gear and looking menacing.

"It's a shit song," says Pete.

"It's not a nice song," says Flimsy.

"I'm not sure our target audience is ready for it," says The Manager.

"But are they ready for the God Song?" is my possibly ill-considered reply. From the direction of one of the oversized sofas that dot the conservatory I detect a rumble. It's Cyrus levering himself up with difficulty from its cavernous cushions. He's almost on his feet, tree-trunk arm raised threateningly in my direction, mouth opening wide as he prepares to deliver a counter-insult. The delay between mouth opening and sound emerging gives The Manager sufficient time to make an intervention.

"Let's do this together," she says. "Brendan, can you get me some paper and pens?"

Brendan rummages around in one of the Conservatory's sideboards and comes up with a block of A4 paper and a pack of children's colouring pens. He hands them to The Manager. She peels off several sheets from the block and hands a sheet to each of us. Then she distributes the colouring pens.

"We're going to vote for the songs on the CD!" she says brightly. "Brendan, do you have any blu-tack?"

Brendan rummages around in the sideboard and comes up with a reel of sellotape. The Manager looks slightly put out.

"Don't blame me if it peels the paint off."

She takes a sheet of A4 and starts writing on it. When she's finished, she tapes the sheet to the wall above the fireplace. On it are twelve songs from the band's set list.

"What I want you to do is write down on your sheet of paper your three best songs. Top song first then the next two in order. You've got twenty minutes. Is that clear? Anyone got any queries?" and she bursts into that characteristic braying donkey laugh.

We congregate around the song list. Giving it a quick scan I notice My Dad was a Cunt conspicuous by its absence. But so is the God Song. Fair enough. Uterque elidat alterum. I decide not to argue the toss. My time will come. Brendan's mum re-appears.

"It's like the fucking Eurovision song contest," mutters Pete between mouthfuls of carrot cake as he picks up his pink felt tip.

An hour later the verdict is in. The Manager stands in the centre of the room to announce the result. This is what she reads out:

Victimised—22 points
Ordinary Madness—18 points
Come to My Rescue—16 points
Words and Intentions—12 points
Dirty Linen—11 points
Fire on Ice—10 points
Hunger—9 points
Hope Street—9 points
Temple of Love—6 points
Full Circle—4 points
Confusion—3 points
Rokbeat—2 points.

A sense of smug satisfaction envelops me like a warm bath at the announcement that Cyrus's two songs sit at the bottom of the pile. It's counter-pointed by a jag of indignation that they would have achieved null points had Cyrus himself not voted for them. So, the EP is now set in stone or polycarbonate plastic if you're being pedantic.

I'd written Victimised in that second stage of grief that follows a traumatic break-up. I first met Adora through my day job when I was teaching at one of the capital's more left-leaning higher education establishments. I'd been parachuted in to replace a Sociology lecturer who'd been suspended for left-leaning tendencies beyond the institution's tolerance thresholds. Only they didn't actually tell me he'd been suspended.

I'd been informed they were one short on their Sociology complement due to human resource issues, so I wasn't prepared for the full-on sit-in that greeted me when I arrived. There were students everywhere in various poses of protest at the Revered Lecturer's suspension—ranging from the two comatose anoraks I had to step over as I came through the entrance to the posse belligerently touting Workers Revolutionary Party banners that confronted me on my way to the Faculty office.

It wasn't the most auspicious of starts. I don't know why but I found myself borrowing the UK Prime Minister John Major's 'Honest John' soap-box routine in the face of this onslaught. I stood up on one of the benches that lined the entrance hall and gave a speech. Honest, it's not my fault. Honest, I'd no idea I'd been brought in to blackleg the Revered Lecturer. Honest, I'm only here temporarily until they reinstate the RL. Honest, I'm happy to turn round and walk back out if that's what you want.

Meanwhile, I'll be in Room 103 should any of you feel the urge to participate in a lecture on Max Weber's Protestant Ethic and Spirit of Capitalism.

I made my way down to Room 103 fully prepared to deliver my least-attended lecture in a long line of poorly-attended lectures. But they'd given me the benefit of the doubt.

After a solitary ten minutes, a couple of students poked their heads around the door and sheepishly shuffled to seats well away from where I was standing. Then more arrived, until Room 103 was at least three-quarters full. In the end, I didn't deliver the Weber lecture. Instead, we talked about the protest and what had led to it, what they wanted to learn and how we'd work together.

Looking back, my Honest John shtick was a master-class in unintended seduction. I seduced myself, I seduced the class and—unwittingly—it turned out I seduced Adora. The last thing on my mind was a scenario in which I end up living with one of my students. But that's what happened. During the six months in which I replaced the Revered Lecturer, I guess we must have laid down the emotional foundations for what later took place.

After she graduated, we met up and took it from there. She moved into my flat. She re-constructed my wardrobe because—in her words—I was on the cusp of fashion. I upgraded from chinos and striped shirts to Nick Cave gear. We went to the US and ate pancakes at New York City diners. We took my kids to see Care Bears. We bought a Wurlitzer 1900 jukebox and installed it in the hallway.

We did the other things that couples are supposed to do. But I guess my perception of what couples are supposed to do didn't align with hers.

I didn't see it coming. There was no obvious sign of anything untoward when I came back to the flat after work. I let myself in and as usual called out I was home. No answer. I walked into the kitchen and put the coffee on. Leafed through the post. Assumed she was out shopping. It was only when I wandered into the bedroom that I realised she was gone. The drawers in the bureau pulled out. The wardrobe doors gaping open.

I walked back into the hallway and registered what I'd missed earlier when I'd first entered the flat. The Wurlitzer had disappeared, along with its hundred-and-four record selections and Cobra pick up. Worth about 12 grand in today's money. A queen amongst jukeboxes.

It wasn't the loss of the Wurlitzer that got to me. It was the loss of the records. In particular Jolene. I remembered all the times the kids were in the flat and we'd put a coin the in the jukebox and select Dolly and sing at the tops of our voices— I'm begging of you please don't take my man. The beauty of it you could open the cash tin and take the coin out and play Jolene as many times as you wanted.

Adora must have had some serious help to hump 150 kilos of steel, chrome and vinyl up the steps and out into the street. I immediately thought of my so-called best mate Steve. Lived down the street. Also one of my former students. Always had our best interests at heart or so he said. Always even-handed in the occasional disputes between Adora and me. It was obvious it was Steve who had organised the annexation of the Wurlitzer.

So Victimised was written in the second stage of break-up grief. It was pure resentment and anger at the disappearance of Adora and the Wurlitzer. It's F sharp, 4/4 starts with a classic verse-verse-chorus-verse-verse-chorus-middle eight then shifts into 24 bars of a completely different riff before reverting to the chorus and reprising it eight times. Here's the lyrics.

I've seen that face before
it doesn't bother me no more
spent too many sleepless nights
to care
I've heard that same old tune
my nervous system is immune
'cause what you do with who

is your affair
Victimised vilified
all the things that you despise
Victimised vilified
seen it written in your eyes
Who's in your story
what precautions are you taking
to make every sentence
justify your action
You call it honesty
and I would call it faking
but then facing facts
was never an attraction
Victimised vilified
all the things that you despise
Victimised vilified
seen it written in your eyes
It's too late
to restore my reputation
love turns to hate
and I'm caught in this transformation
And the grass is always greener
on the other side of town
and the air is so much cleaner
if you turn round from what's going down
and things are so much better
than they ever were before
when you live up to the letter
not the spirit of the law
but the truth hurts everybody
colours everything you see
constant static in your headphones
is it really what you wanted to be
Victimised, vilified
Victimised vilified
all the things that you despise

Victimised vilified
seen it written in your eyes.

Apart from a couple of lines from The Police, I sneaked in that seemed to fit the structure of the song I thought it was lyrically quite original. Musically, it opened up spaces the band could dive into. The slow opening bars allowed Pete to weave a web of jazz-root arpeggios, Brendan to anchor the song down with a bass riff you couldn't escape from and Cyrus to make his mark with a series of elaborate drum shuffles. As it progressed, it picked up speed, while still retaining a laid-back almost Latin feel, bringing in Max's virtuoso sax solo and Flimsy's haunting backing harmonies to take the song to its climax.

'Come to My Rescue' was written in the third stage of break-up—that doom-time when you lose all sense of dignity and emotionally soil yourself by doing desperate and degrading things you regret forever. It's a kind of limbo-land where, rationally, you know you've moved on from denial and anger but still retain the irrational conviction that somehow you can put together a convincing argument for things to go back to how they were before.

The textbook term for this stage is called Bargaining. But 'bargaining' assumes a more or less equal distribution of power between the bargainer and bargainee. As everyone who's on the being left side of a break-up knows, being left means you have no bargaining power at all.

Essentially, you've been left. So you come up with a series of actions that in your head look like they're negotiations but in fact are pathetic attempts at coercion. Like the text you send to your ex-lover after two bottles of wine and a whisky chaser. The text that starts with a solicitous how are you doing and ends with the excruciatingly infantile I miss you so much. The title of 'Come to My Rescue' says it all.

I got the idea for 'Ordinary Madness' after watching a series of news reports on what seemed to be an epidemic of global atrocities—from mass-scale genocide in Rwanda and Bosnia to the everyday brutality meted out by law enforcement agencies on city streets from Baltimore to Bristol.

I remember one commentator referring to the banality of inhumanity. The capacity of humans to administer barbarism so routinely that in the end, it becomes normalised. Ordinary. Into my head came this image of God, sitting in his deck chair on Mount Olympus, watching day time television and becoming increasingly incensed at the behaviour of the mortals he'd created. So, he calls up a chat line to make his views heard. Then he's put in touch with another punter who wants to express his opinion.

By pure chance, it's the Lord of the Flies. In constructing the Devil's persona I'd probably borrowed from Jack Nicholson's portrayal of Daryl van Horne in *The Witches of Eastwick*. He's urbane, laconic, beautifully turned-out and consummately street-wise. In contrast, God is an indignant shit-kicker. He wears home-spun dungarees, reads the Daily Mail and can't understand why humans are habitually, routinely, ordinarily fucking mad.

The song is in a very simple format. Verse-verse-chorus-verse-chorus-verse-chorus-verse-chorus. There's only four chords—C#/F#, then C#/G#, followed by D#, F# and G#. But the BPM at 130 beats per minute is challenging, especially for singers.

If you're not careful, the syllables don't keep up with the time and trip over each other, so the words end up coming out as an unintelligible mush. But it's a godsend for Pete with its underbelly of repeating cascading township guitar arpeggios. Here's the lyrics:

God was talking to the devil on a chat line telephone
he said it's good to hear somebody I've been feeling so alone
we've got so much in common we've got so much to discuss
let's leave the lies to politicians and the policy to us
genocide in Africa there's hatred and there's war
there's a poor man in the city kicked and beaten by the law
here's twenty thousand women violated and abuse
hey why I hear you laughin' there's no call to be amused
Devil, he say
Ordinary Madness
It's only Ordinary Madness
God was walking with the Devil on a sleazy city street
where the low-life no-hope people beg like mongrels at your feet
God say who that bog-eyed zombie come shufflin' up to me
he's a case for medication how come he still walkin' free?
Devil smile and say
Ordinary Madness
It's only Ordinary Madness
God was drinking with the Devil in an exclusive chic cafe

he said there must be something we can do
things don't have to be this way
it's a senseless way of livin' it's a dirty crying shame
but I've heard it whispered on the streets
it's you should take the blame
Devil shook his head
Ordinary Madness
It's only Ordinary Madness
I could say that you're old-fashioned but I would not be so crude
don't believe what's in the papers
I've been sadly misconstrued
take some of this white powder it's just what you're lookin' for
it's the only real salvation the only proven cure
for Ordinary Madness
Ordinary Madness.

Two weeks later and The Manager has booked a studio to record the Victimised EP. It's not Abbey Road, but the client list is intimidating. Nina Simone. Jimmy Cliff, Gloria Estefan, Ben E. King, Gladys Knight, Tom Jones, Patti Smith, Jack Bruce, Paul Weller, The Specials, Ian Dury, Courtney Pine.

"Do you want analogue or digital?" asks the sound engineer, looking down at me over a vast bank of equipment, its lights twinkling and oscillating—like a starship navigating an unchartered Galaxy. I feel the need to rope Duff and Brendan into the conversation.

Apparently, we have the option of using digital software—Pro Tools—to produce the CD. Alternatively, we could do the session in analogue—which means it's recorded in real-time, as it sounds to the human ear. I have no clue. I'm a sociologist. Leave it to the experts. They decide on a hybrid. We record in analogue. Then we mix and master it in DAT—digital audio tape. I wouldn't know a DAT from my anus, but it looks like they know what they're doing.

I spend most of the first day of recording not doing any recording. Not knowing anything about recording, I'd assumed we'd all get together in the studio, run through a practice session with a song, do a few more practice sessions to iron out the creases then play a final session of the song and record it. Job done.

Duff, Brendan and the sound engineer had to sit me down and gently explain to me, as if to a toddler, that a recording session was in fact a sequence of mini-sessions in which different bits of the song are recorded. Then, at the end, there's a big finale—a mega-session where all the previous bits are mixed together—and, bingo, you end up with your perfectly polished meisterwerk.

You start with the rhythm section. I guess it makes sense because the rhythm section provides the spine of the song. Its heartbeat. If you don't get the rhythm right then the other sections—the lead guitar, the keyboard, the sax and the singers—have nothing to grip onto. You build the rhythm section piece by piece, layering the bass drum, snare, toms, high hats, cymbals and the bass guitar, on top of each other—like laminating a floor—until you get the solid foundation the band needs to build on.

Then the lead guitarist comes in and adds their sparkle to the mix, followed by the remaining instruments—the keyboards and horns. Then you do the overdubbing and the arrangements.

Basically, the overdubbing involves layering all the different bits already recorded on top of each other so you get a rich, full, combined sound. The arrangements involve messing around with what comes out of the overdubbing. You re-arrange bits, you cut bits, you add bits and you put in special effects. It's only after you've finished the instrumental arrangements that the vocalists are allowed in.

It looks like I have a lot of thumb-twiddling to look forward to. I go to the bar and get myself a coffee. Come back and watch Cyrus and Brendan do their thing in the studio through the glass partition. Put on some headphones to hear what's going on. All I can make out are thumps and rattles. Disjointed bass guitar twangs. Go to the bar and get myself a coffee. Sit down in the reception area and flick through a copy of Private Eye that someone's left there. Go back to the studio and watch Cyrus and Brendan do their thing.

By the time they call me to do the first vocal take for 'Victimised', it's already six in the evening. They put me in a soundproofed booth at the side of the main studio. There's a Neumann U87 set up on a stand with a filter attached to stop me from popping plosives. There's something about being alone in the booth, without the protection of the band, that makes me feel nervous.

They're all looking expectantly at me from the studio. I start to adjust the Neumann's height to get it closer to my vocal cords but my nervousness makes me fumble and I almost dislodge it from its stand. I need to calm down. The sound engineer directs my attention to the headphones hung over the mic stand. I put them on and his voice comes through, startlingly loud, "OK. I'm gonna give you a guide track to work from. Just basic rhythm and melody line. No frills to distract you. I'll count you in and on three, you start singing."

I nod hesitantly. I'm not feeling confident about this. I'm concentrating so hard on remembering the opening line that I'm fractionally late on the count. Now, I've put myself under pressure. I'm struggling to catch up and I'm stumbling over syllables, finishing lines too early. It surprises me that I manage to complete the whole track.

The engineer plays it back. It's on speaker as well as my headphones so the whole band can hear it. Without any accompaniment whatsoever, my voice is exposed. I'm as embarrassed as if I were standing there naked. My vocals are all over the place. My voice sounds reedy and fluttery as if I've been running for a bus. I'm slurring lines like a drunk. I'm not hitting the high notes.

I can see the engineer shaking his head in the studio. He flips on the intercom. "You're not breathing properly. That's why the strength and the tone are uneven. It's why some of the notes are off-key. You need to have enough breath to hit the notes properly—especially the high ones. Let's do a quick breathing exercise before we start again."

He takes me through some deep breathing. I remember what they told me at the yoga Sivananda Centre. Control the breath. Take it in slowly through the belly. Then command it to move up through the diaphragm and into the upper chest. Relax. Let the breath permeate your body. I let Sivananda take me over. It seems to do the trick.

The second take of the track is much better. As I breathe better I'm building confidence. As I build confidence, I build momentum. By the fifth take, the engineer's happy, the band's happy. I'm happy. I vacate the booth and Flimsy slips in to add the backing vocals. By the time we've repeated the whole process for 'Ordinary Madness', it's after midnight. Time to call it a day.

"Take it easy tomorrow," Cyrus tells me as I move to the exit. "We've got plenty to do on 'Come to my Rescue'. Have a lie-in. We won't need you or Flimsy until after lunch."

The next day I take Cyrus's advice. It's a Sunday. Normally, a mooching around day. I get up late and fix some breakfast. Spend some time going through the lyrics on Come to my Rescue. I want to make sure I've nailed them down so I won't have to worry about fluffing the lines when I'm in that booth. I decide to get down to the studio before lunch, even though the vocalists aren't needed until later. I want to understand more about how this recording lark works for future reference. But when I walk through the studio entrance, I see Flimsy is already there. She's standing in reception, talking to Cyrus.

She clocks me and beams this horribly smug smile in my direction, like the one my sister gave me when I woke up one Christmas morning to find she'd eaten all my tangerines. Beside her, Cyrus is twinkling, like a belisha beacon.

"Afternoon, boss," he says as I walk up to them. "We've cracked it. Victimised is all done. Flimsy came up with some great ideas. It's a corking track. Just wait till you hear it. You'll love it."

It's obvious I'm looking underwhelmed at the prospect, but I follow them to the studio. Put on the headphones. Victimised comes streaming through. As I listen I have to admit it's sounding great. Timed to perfection. Not a beat out of place. The bass line is beautifully clean. Pete's guitar riffs are muscular instead of fussy. Band pulling together. Tight as a bottle. It's only when I get to the outro that the conspiracy reveals itself.

I've been done up like an Arbroath smokie. In my absence, Flimsy's gone and added an extra eight bars at the end of the song, featuring repeated variations of the chorus 'Victimised, vilified, all the things that you despise—' It's actually a stunning performance but she's done exactly what she set out to do. She's snatched the song out of my hands and annexed it. Made it hers instead of mine.

The meme that will now worm its way into a listener's head after the song has finished will be Flimsy's sibilant hiss—Victimisssssed. Not my smooth vocals. Inside, I'm volcanic. I want to take that stupid scarf she's wearing, wrap it around her neck and squeeze hard. But the entire band is giving itself a self-congratulatory pat on the back.

Then to add spice to the insult, the band proudly reveals the mangling it's inflicted on 'Ordinary Madness'. Not only have they extended the outro, they've put in a trombone riff over the guitar arpeggios, preceded by a trombone accompaniment in all of the choruses. A fucking trombone! And it's a real trombone, not a sound sampled from the Yamaha. Which means it booms in and out like a steamer's fog horn.

But there's nothing I can do. It's a done deal. If I protest and insist on restoring Victimised to its original format, featuring me, numero uno, on the outro it'll look not only petty but dictatorial. The same goes for 'Ordinary Madness'. Better to bow out gracefully and store up the latest slight for later.

Revenge is a dish best served on the red hot coals of the Glastonbury Pyramid Stage at a point in the imminent future.

We spend the rest of the day laying down Come to my Rescue, then mixing and mastering the three songs. It's two in the morning when we finish. I feel I know what it's like to spend two days in the labour ward. But it's a wrap. The Victimised EP exists. It's real. The ephemeral things we rehearse in the studio and perform in a grotty pub in Islington have been transformed into digital matter. Next, the matter will be solidified—converted into a thing you hold in your hand and slot into your CD player.

We play the Trolley Stop the next day. The Trolley is a home fixture. Just down the road from where I live. I'm known there, so I want the band to put in a good performance. I don't fancy being confronted in the queue at Sainsburys by some muppet who says, "I know you. You sing in that band. I saw you at the Trolley last week. You were really shit."

Turn up at the Trolley early to check out the band on the undercard. They're called Tiger Lillies. We do the sound check then retire to the bar to watch them. I've never seen anything like it. To call it a band would be an understatement.

For one, they don't actually sing. The lead singer caterwauls his way through a set of numbers that make your hair stand on end. It's more like a music-hall act. They do mime. They do cabaret. They do what looks like art installations. They do a number that features Jesus on the Cross with nails hammered into him. They play the accordion in Bertold Brecht style. The audience loves it. I love it too but when they complete their set and retire off-stage, I'm left with a terrible sense of inadequacy. How can we compete with this bonkers act that makes us look like Teletubbies?

Go on stage. Packed house. It's always a good idea to get a feel for the audience. You need to have a sense of how you can best engage with it. Whether you should treat it as your friend. Talk to it as if you're having an intimate drink in a bar. Or whether you should keep it at a distance. As if you're giving a lecture to a bunch of half-wits who are there to be enlightened.

You take your cue from their signals. Whether they look bored or expectant. Whether they're milling around or passive. Their body language. How pissed they are. From where I'm standing the audience looks and feels a bit lairy. There's a buzz of uncontrolled energy in the air.

I'm coming to the end of 'Full Circle' when a fat bloke draped in a flag with a huge red dragon painted in the middle of it whirls onto the stage. There's a conspicuous absence of security at the Trolley Stop so his line of approach towards me goes unimpeded. He grabs me by the waistcoat. "Boyo," he says exhaling a cloud of concentrated London Pride into my face. "I've got a request. It's for the girlfriend. She's called Abigail. Play one for her."

I'm about to politely decline the invitation but the pint of London Pride clenched in a fist the size of a bunch of bananas changes my mind.

I do a hasty confab with the band. We never do requests. None of the material remotely relates to Abigail. I peer at the crowd Fat Bloke has re-joined. Register he's with a sizeable posse of other fat blokes draped in flags with red dragons painted in the middle. There's a blonde girl next to the posse looking expectantly at me.

Then it clicks. The England-Wales rugby match at Twickenham. Thousands of taffies invading London. Somehow a remnant of the horde has meandered its way from the west and is watering its hole in the East End. They're looking pissed up and dangerous. Then an inspiration. Before settling on Cantaloupe as our set opener we'd incorporated various covers into the set for insurance. One of the favourites was Joe Jackson's *Fools in Love*. We play it now and again if we're running out of numbers. The killer line, repeated three times and ending the song is "I should know because this fool's in love again."

I give the band the nod. *Fools in Love* it is. I get to the killer line and sing 'I should know because my name is Abigail'. As I sing it out a beatific grin spreads across the face of Fat Bloke. He projects puppy eyes at the blond girl and they crush together as the Taffy posse explodes into applause. When we get offstage there's a row of twenty pints waiting for us on the tab at the bar.

The band started with the ashram. The ashram started with the Damascene moment of self-realisation in the Charlie Chaplin pub. I needed to get out of my stuckness to understand stuckness. I needed to retreat somewhere so off the grid the stuckness couldn't get to me. Like a yurt camp in the foothills of the Himalayas. I started a search for ashram opportunities.

They were all offering a similar shtick. Up at 5 AM. Meditation. Two hours of Asanas and pranayama. Breakfast. More yoga. Chanting. Lunch (vegetarian). Lectures on yoga. More yoga. Silent walk. Dinner (vegetarian). More chanting. Lights out at 8 PM. Z-meditation—the joy of de-conditioning—looked as good as any. It extended me the possibility of completely eliminating suffering from my life. A two week retreat in the solitude of the Himalayan foothills would do the trick. Freedom, Bliss and Awareness were not mere esoteric words. I could experience them as my true identities.

The only requirements were objectivity and sincerity. To join Z-meditation, I first had to do a Simple Awareness Exercise. This would tell me how restless I was in my thoughts. I would understand that most of the time, I lived in a state of daydreaming and unless I learned to snap myself out of it, I could not be peaceful and happy.

The exercise went like this. I had to inhale, whilst saying 'Om' in my mind. On exhaling, I had to do reverse counting starting from one hundred—one count with each breath. If, on the way, some other thoughts disturbed me, I had to note them down and start all over again from one hundred. If I had feelings, I had to note them down too. I had to do this for one hour.

I did my first Om. I got to twenty-eight before I ran out of breath. No restless thoughts had disturbed me. I did my second Om. I got to twenty-six before I ran out of breath. Again, I experienced no restless thoughts. I tried a third Om. Then a fourth. On the tenth Om, it dawned on me that I wasn't troubled by restless thoughts. I was troubled by shortness of breath. All those hours smoking Embassy Regal in school breaks had come back to haunt me.

I needed a taster before I signed up for the hardcore. Instead of the Himalayan foothills, I put my name down for a Yoga Weekend in Putney. Nestling alongside the River Thames, the Sivananda Yoga Centre occupied a substantial property in a quietly expensive residential side-street, rubbing shoulders with four-by-fours, braying South Africans on gap year and plum-voiced rowers in Lycra.

The Centre offered an intensive taster curriculum more attuned to the London lifestyle. It started at a more civilised hour—ten-thirty—than its Himalayan counterpart. First, there was a ninety-minute session of Yoga. This covered the twelve classic Asanas of old-school Hatha. Headstands and shoulder-stands. Fish and Cobra. Locust and Crow. Prefaced by pranayama and Sun Salutations and ending with relaxation. Then lunch (vegetarian). A Talk on Yoga. A Silent Walk. Then more Yoga. All repeated the following day.

Using public transport to travel East to West across London to the Sivananda Centre would take around two hours, what with the Tube improvement work, railway line closures and bus route suspensions that had become a weekend way of life in the city.

I decided to go in the Citroen, resolving to park it discreetly out of sight, for fear its decaying decadence would offend the frugal sensibilities of the Centre's incumbents. I stowed my cigarettes, mobile phone and credit cards in the trunk—a symbolic disrobing of unneeded accoutrements that signalled the start of my de-conditioning. I stole to the entrance, took a shallow, un-Yogic breath and walked in.

The Centre was not how I had imagined it. There were no shaven-headed bhagwans in orange togas intoning Hare Krishna. No concrete cells with straw mattresses. Entrance to the Centre's inner core was afforded by a spacious, glass-walled foyer with reception desk and shop shelves stacked with books, DVDs, yoga mats, yoga gear and yoga trinkets. A sliding door opened out onto a small courtyard neatly landscaped with pot plants, water features and garden chairs. Friendly staff wearing yellow t-shirts stencilled with the Centre's logo greeted new arrivals. This was the soft, public face of Hatha yoga.

The private face was more unforgiving. I remember one of my fellow weekenders declaring, as we sat, cross-legged and shell-shocked after a third session of headstands and cobras, that she he had friends in the Territorial Army who had a far easier time on assault courses. I remember promising myself that if I survived the weekend, I would get three Oms tattooed on my body. One on each forearm and one between my eyebrows.

Pranayama. Sounds innocuous, doesn't it? Like some honey-coated waffle. Wrong. The first rule of Pranayama is—don't do it at home. Not unless you live close to an ambulance station. The second rule of Pranayama is—don't do it if you have a sinus condition. Snot loves suction. You end up snorting and gasping and turning blue. Your co-Yogis are all looking around wondering if something's gone wrong with the radiators.

Pranayama is a set of breathing techniques. According to the Centre's brochure, it revitalises the body, steadies the emotions and creates clarity of mind. It increases the flow of 'Prana'—the life-sustaining force that flows through the body through a network of channels—'nadis'.

For the beginner, there are two breathing techniques designed to increase your Prana. The first one is Kapalabhati or short breathing. Imagine an old steam engine leaving a station. The engineer releases super-heated steam from the boiler. It pushes pistons. They strain to shift the huge, inert bulk of the engine and its carriages. A puff of smoke and steam and the train slowly moves forward. Chuff! It leaves the sidings. Gains momentum. Chuff! Chuff! It increases speed. Soon, it is thundering along through lush countryside. Chuff! Chuff! Chuff!

That's what Kapalabhati is like. Suck in air. Use the diaphragm and abdomen to push it like a piston. Move that resistant bulk of a body out of its inertia. Chuff! That's good. Now, you're gaining momentum. Push that diaphragm harder and faster. Chuff! Chuff! Now, you've got speed. Chuff! Chuff! Chuff! Only your diaphragm is not made out of cast iron. Your lungs are not pistons. It's exhausting.

Four rounds of it felt like the four rounds I did with a future British ABA champion at Kirkby Boxing Club. At the end of it, the future British ABA champion dropped his gloves and said, "No offence, mate. You've got bollocks, but your boxing's shit."

The second breathing technique is Anuloma Viloma—alternate nostril breathing. You inhale through one nostril, retain the breath and exhale through the other nostril. The left nostril connects to your 'Ida' nadi and the right nostril connects to your 'Pingala' nadi. It goes like this.

Inhale through the left nostril, closing the right with the thumb, to the count of four. Hold the breath, closing both nostrils, to the count of sixteen. Exhale through the right nostril, closing the left with the ring and little fingers, to the count of eight. Inhale through the right nostril, keeping the left nostril closed with the ring and little fingers, to the count of four. Hold the breath, closing both nostrils, to the count of sixteen. Exhale through the left nostril, keeping the right closed with the thumb, to the count of eight.

The Yogis believe that doing Anuloma Viloma harmonises the function of both sides of the brain so you end up with a nice balance between creativity and logical thinking. At the same time, it calms the mind as well as the nervous system.

For me, it had the opposite effect. I kept getting the wrong finger up the wrong nostril. I panicked. Hyper-ventilating and over-oxygenating, I regressed into my birth canal terror, drowning in amniotic fluid. It was like my first experience of scuba diving when fear of drowning leads you to breathe faster than the regulator is designed to work.

I tried to cheat, surreptitiously exposing a sliver of nostril to the atmosphere in order to suck in more air. But paranoia set in. I was convinced the watching instructors were attuned to our every move. This made me more anxious. My sympathetic nervous system kicked in. It cranked up my cardiovascular response and demanded even more air. Shaken and breathless, I was in no state for the rigours of the Asanas that followed.

There are old photographs lining the walls of the Sivananda Centre studios of its founder—Swami Sivananda—taken on what looks like a beach in Goa before the tourists got there. He stands out not only because of the chiselled features and air of authority he exudes but because of the large overcoat he's wearing in the searing heat, in contrast to the skimpy loin cloths and boxer shorts worn by his followers.

All eyes in the photograph are fixed on a figure on a rock. It looks like something Anthony Gormally would fabricate out of old scrap iron and an Arts Council grant. The figure has human form but in reverse. Its arms are its legs. Its legs are curved over its inverted head. This is the Scorpion—the Vrischika asana.

It's called the Scorpion because the body resembles a scorpion with its tail arched above its head ready to sting its victim. Performing it leads to an impressively long list of benefits, according to those in the know. It strengthens the arms, shoulders, back and fully expands the lungs. It stretches the neck, spine and chest and the abdominal muscles. It increases blood flow to the brain and pituitary glands and revitalises all the body systems. It increases circulation in the lower limbs and the abdomen and tones the reproductive organs. It improves balance, concentration and peace of mind. Hecapedia—the ayurvedic medicine website—gives the Scorpion a difficulty tariff of seven out of ten, observing it's not as difficult as it may at first seem.

I have no evidence to challenge this claim. Before you reach the summit of the Scorpion, you must first traverse the foothills of the headstand. The headstand is exactly what it says on the tin. You stand on your head. Then you extend the posture into the Scorpion. I never made it out of the foothills. For twenty minutes, I strained and groaned but I couldn't get my legs above my head. All I got was a throbbing pain across the width of my upper back. The instructor, a chirpy Lithuanian, made my excuses for me. I had the wrong back shape. It was too rounded. Not for the first time in my life, I'd been given a dispensation.

Asanas are a bit like the stress techniques used by interrogators to soften up interrogees. By the time they're finished, you allow yourself to be led like a baby to the Lecture Room. You sit cross-legged in a stress posture on wafer-thin cushions set over a hard parquet floor. A lecturer perches comfortably in full Lotus position next to a flip chart. His head is close-cropped. His skin has that unfeasibly healthy sheen that comes from an animal-free diet, regular sleep and total abstinence. His eyes glow with the sparkle of the converted.

He tells us about the benefits of Yoga. Not just the generic benefits, but the specific benefits. Of each of the twelve classic postures in the Hatha yogic cycle. In great detail. The physiological benefits. The psychological benefits. The emotional benefits. The spiritual benefits. I lost track of time. I entered into a trance. For one ground-swallowing moment, my mind flipped into the fleeting illusion it had entered the state of Enlightenment all Yogis strive for. It was brought back to earth by the sharp cramp that had gripped my buttocks.

Lunch brought overdue relief. It was preceded by a communal mantra—the Hatha equivalent of saying Grace. We all had to join hands and give thanks for our food. I scuttled off to the toilet returning just when the Mantra had finished. The food was colourful, tasty and nourishing, although I was so hungry I could have eaten my own arm.

After lunch, I stammered a faltering excuse—something about an important phone call—and stepped outside into the street. The city leered at me knowingly. Its petty compromises and indiscretions wrapped themselves around me, embracing me like an old drinking partner. I slunk over to the parked Citroen, opened the trunk, extracted my cigarettes and lighter and darted around the corner, smoking furiously. I snuck back in through a side entrance, in time to see my fellow-yogis donning coats and gloves. It was time for the Silent Walk.

Silence has a big voice in Yoga. In some interpretations of Vedantic philosophy, silence seems to be used interchangeably with 'Prana'—the life-force. Silence is both godhead and soul; the aim and purpose of existence. The Sanskrit for 'silence' is derived from the root 'mun'—to measure. What this means, I guess, is that silence is a benchmark of how far the Yogic disciple has travelled on the path to 'One-ness'.

The more silence is understood, engaged with and used—for instance through meditation—the greater the disciple's spiritual progress. It's easy to see where this preoccupation with quiescence comes from. On one level, it fits with the Vedantic principles of simplicity and austerity. Reverence for silence represents a search for an antidote to the vacuity of modern life, with its cacophony of chatter; its tsunami of radio jingles, TV drivel, Twittersphere babble; its bubbled earbuds; its overwhelming aural diversions.

Modern life is anti-silence. It's the sound of the bazaar. Sound sells just as much as sex. Anti-silence lies at the heart of the transactions we make every day as conspicuous consumers. It's there, upfront, as we soak up the adverts between reality shows in front of the TV, between bite-sized chunks of YouTube videos.

It's used less brazenly, but more insidiously, in the mouths of actors, talk-show hosts and social media influencers, as they peddle whatever zeitgeist is currently in vogue.

At the time I was struggling with stuckness in the UK, the prevailing zeitgeist was 'Cool Britannia'. The driving force of 'Cool Britannia' was a Labour government, determined never again to re-live the experience of twenty years in the Opposition wilderness. It used a sophisticated and highly-effective media machine to reinforce and manipulate the image that had been swallowed by the electorate of a fresh, young modernising government led by a fresh, young, modernising Prime Minister.

It created a political and cultural greenhouse in which new iconic specimens that amplified that image could flourish. Perhaps fittingly, given the new zeitgeist's obsession with irony, the first beneficiary was an ice cream manufactured by the US company, Ben and Jerry. The phrase 'Cool Britannia'—itself borrowed from a song title by the newly cool 1960s cult group 'Bonzo Dog Doo Dah Band'—was coined by an American lawyer living in London, Sarah Moynihan-Williams, as a winning entry in a Ben and Jerry's competition.

Endorsed as a perfect slogan to encapsulate an increasingly self-confident Britishness, Cool Britannia unleashed a wave of products and postures on an unprepared world, bequeathing it Britpop, the Spice Girls, Damian Hirst and *Loaded* Magazine. It sanctioned the proliferation of 'Laddist' culture. Films like *Lock, Stock and Two Smoking Barrels* directed by Guy Ritchie, re-invented and re-packaged an earlier zeitgeist—the *Swinging London* of the 1960s, drawing on previous cinematic icons like *The Italian Job*.

On the surface, 'Lock, Stock' was inventive, new—wave cinema shot in vaudeville screen-wash using over-cranked and under-cranked production tricks borrowed from adverts and pop promos. Its flimsy storyline, superficial characterisation and comedy ultra-violence were not only forgiven but applauded by its many admirers as illustrations of its audacity, verve and wit.

But what really lay behind the ligaments of the film, with its East-end warehouse sets and retro-Mod fashion, was a sales pitch. At its hollow centre, Lock, Stock was a long advert for loft conversions and male grooming. And the sales pitch was in the script. Through the Mockney dialogue invented by Ritchie, the private school-educated son of an advertising executive, characters like Bacon, Soap and Big Chris product-placed a Cool Britannia lifestyle of big pay-days, big suits and big jewellery.

'Lad' Magazines like *Loaded* reinforced the branding through editorials, articles, advertising spreads and through their whole style and tone. In their converted dockside apartments, nouveau riche barrow boys from Goldman Sachs and old Etonians from BBH alike gobbled it all up, the whole sanitised gangster fantasy. In the bars that had sprung up around Hoxton and Shoreditch, formerly derelict and newly-gentrified areas of London's East End, they spread the word, chattering away in the now ubiquitous Mockney vernacular; washing it down with over-priced Budweiser.

In embracing silence, I think the Yogis were making a statement about the way in which sound and language, articulate desire. If desire is apprehended through vision, to misquote Marcus Aurelius, as Thomas Harris did in *Silence of the Lambs*, then it is expressed through speech. We covet things when we set eyes on them. Then we talk about the things we covet. How many conversations have you had with someone who talks about their latest acquisition? How many conversations have you had with someone who talks enviously about someone else's acquisition?

Speech—on TV, on the radio, in the cinema, in print, around the dinner table, in the pub, in tweets—is viral in nature. It spreads our desires. Yogis think that by cutting out speech we can cut out the desires that divert us from spiritual fulfilment. As Swami Sivananda says, "Desire is poverty. Desire is the greatest impurity of the mind. Desire is the motive force for action. Desire in the mind is the real impurity. Even a spark of desire is a very great evil."

In the Yogic mind desire, speech and ego are all linked. When we desire things, we want them for ourselves. Desire is inherently selfish. When we speak, it is typically because we want to express our individuality; our self-absorption; our desire to dominate others. Speech is the language of the Me. Silence is the language of the One. It brings serenity, calmness and leads to inner spiritual strength. Silence is peace.

I half-heartedly join hands with my fellow-Yogis for the chant that precedes the Silent Walk. We're given our walk instructions. No chat. Concentrate on breathing. Focus on the inner world not the outer. This is not as easy as it sounds when you're shuffling along the Thames walkway, hands in pockets, buffeted by a chill early Spring wind.

There were too many distractions. Seagulls fighting for scraps exposed by the receding tidal flow. Oarsmen lowering boats into the water. The river was in rude health. People chasing dogs. Dogs chasing birds. The careless banality of a

Saturday off. We turned away from the river into a park, criss-crossed by pathways churned up by the rain.

Passing a vast expanse of playing fields, I was mugged by nostalgia. This was where I came from. From some old memory chest, I extracted images of Saturday afternoons on a muddy football pitch in woolly-back land, chasing a hopeless punt from the midfield. As I walked in silence past the jostling players and the shouting spectators, I felt a tug of envy. I wanted to be pulled into their shrill inanity; enveloped in their crude vitality. I wanted to compete. I wanted to be in there, kicking and fighting in the mud.

But I was a Yoga Tourist. A Day Yipper. It felt like commitment aversion. "It's not you," I said to the One-ness, inflexing the pronoun with theatrical bathos, "It's me."

Dawdling along watching the footballers, I'd been left behind by my companions. When I caught up with them, they were standing in a circle around a big tree, chanting an Om. I lurked behind, furtively, took out my phone and pretended I'd just received another emergency call. It was all too alien. Maybe I was just as much a prisoner as everyone else, caught in the chat; stuck in the gangster fantasy.

After the final Yoga session, I felt like I'd been paroled. I declined the smiling offer of the optional Meditation and headed instead for the Que Viet, on the Kingsland Road, back in the East End. Over a dish of soft-shell crab and a glass of Malbec, I pondered other paths to Enlightenment. Then—in my head— I started to form the band. The antidote to silence.

April

Porno Dave has offered to do the cover for the CD. Porno Dave—legendary skank-artist. Consummate opportunist. We were once driving the Citroen through teuchter territory on the East Coast of Scotland when a pheasant shoots out across the road straight under the wheels. Stop the car screams Dave. He gets out, leaving me wondering if he's aiming to apply first aid. After a couple of minutes, he gets back in and dumps the bird's carcase on the back seat. That's me dinner sorted, he says.

Porno Dave. Purveyor of avant-garde dressed up in a latex bodysuit. He once persuaded me to assist him in a Living Art Installation on the London Underground. We bought around five kilos of old cut-offs from the local butcher, put them in carrier bags with a note inside that said 'Meat is Art—Art is Meat' and left them in various Tube trains. I never understood the aesthetic message but it certainly had an impact. We ended up bringing the entire network to a halt. The Met's anti-terrorist unit, who'd spent the previous two weeks battling an increasingly high-profile IRA terrorist campaign in the capital, were not amused.

At art school, Porno's MA dissertation was an installation called 'Scopophilia'. From a seat in a claustrophobic booth constructed from plywood, the viewer (or more accurately the voyeur) puts their eye to a lens and, via an ingenious construction of telescopic pipework, is transported to a peep-hole through which they spy their neighbour in her bathroom angling the ridge of the bathtub like a hurdler.

In the background, an endless loop of concatenated frames spliced from gonzo porn movies projects onto one of the walls of the booth. He came to my house to do the gonzo edit and spent the best part of forty-eight hours locked up in the spare bedroom, emerging at the end of the edit with eyes the size of the moon. I'm in two minds about accepting Porno's offer. I'm aware that his innovative approach to erotica could be construed as misogyny.

On the other hand, our design budget is non-existent and he's offering his services for free. I make the calculation. Cash trumps misogyny.

Porno comes to the house and retires to the spare bedroom. He emerges at breakfast and slaps the proof of the Victimised CD cover onto the table. It looks like something Seurat might have knocked up after a night on the Absinthe. Everything is pixelated. It's hard to discern any shapes but you can just about make out a figure. Probably human. Possibly female. Above the figure's head in big bold Bauhaus 93 font the title track screams out—Victimised!

Porno explains the concept. The pixilation represents the atomism of post-modern culture. As humans, we constantly strive to retain our human form against the onslaught of forces that try to disintegrate us. The only thing that will save us is the healing power of women. Only they have the holistic vision to rescue us from imminent apocalypse. The female figure is struggling to protect her atoms against the maelstrom and is striving to condense them together so she can solidify counter-opposition to anarchy.

At the same time, the atomised female figure speaks to the ways in which female sexuality is appropriated and misused to serve male patriarchy so that women's bodies and minds themselves disintegrate and serve no purpose but to bend to the male whim, as is evidenced by the fact that the images on the cover have been lifted from gonzo movies.

I'm not convinced, but we're badly in need of a CD cover and strapped for cash.

"Thanks, Dave," I say slipping him a bacon sandwich. "I owe you one," although we both know that in the bank of favours, he's seriously overdrawn.

The next band rehearsal provides an opportunity for us to collectively review the CD cover. The initial response is not promising. As always Pete is the first to voice an opinion.

"What the fuck is that?" he says, stabbing a finger at what may or may not be a female.

"It's a metaphor for the atomism of post-modern culture," I respond, drawing a circle around the androgynous image as if illustrating a tank manoeuvre to a bunch of Army recruits.

"It's shit," he says, folding his arms aggressively.

Flimsy takes a similarly negative position. "Why can't we just have a photo of the band on the cover?" she asks.

"Because it's boring and we're not photogenic like *the Beatles*," I respond. "We need something different. Something radical. Something edgy. Something arty."

The rest of the band can't make their minds up whether it's complete crap or the new Peter Blake. It takes The Manager's intervention to endow Porno's masterpiece with the official seal of approval.

"I think it's great," she brays. "It's just so, so—Victimised."

The Manager sends the artwork and the DAT tape to a CD production company in Ireland. Two weeks later I get a delivery. Ten anonymous-looking cardboard cartons. I open one up. Inside, fifty pristine copies of 'Victimised', each beautifully cello-wrapped. I take one out. Porno Dave's androgynous figure rears up at me like a praying mantis. Rock and Roll.

The Manager sends the CD to the inner and outer reaches of the Music Universe, enclosed in a Press Pack intended to endear us to prospective record companies. From a vantage point two decades later, the Press Pack could charitably be described as naive-but-sweet. Flimsy finally got the image she'd been denied with the CD cover.

The front page is dominated by a single black-and-white photograph of the band. It freeze frames our various gauche poses in perpetuity. I'm supposed to be in the foreground as the band's centrepiece—Il Duce, the lead singer—but I'm upstaged by yet another shameless attempt by Flimsy to hog the limelight. She's decided to go for a wacky femme fatale look. It's like a cross between those poses the Beatles used in A Hard Day's Night when they were photographed at strange but radical angles and the gushing sexuality you get in early Madonna.

She's wearing a silk blouse that culminates in a bizarre neck ruff that looks like a turkey on its way to the abattoir and she's reclining at an angle of forty-five degrees, held up by the perspiring sax player. I'm trying to look cool. Classic white T-shirt (Next). Black waistcoat (Oxfam). Black jeans (Next). Topped with a hat I found in a junk shop in Mile End that looks like a cross between a fez and a kufi—a panic buy intended to camouflage my increasingly thinning hair.

Flimsy, I and the sax player are flanked by the keyboard player on one side and the bass player on the other—both looking as if they've just graduated from kindergarten. Behind us, Cyrus parodies his towering presence whilst giving out the uncompromising impression of a towering presence.

It wasn't the band photograph that caused the problem with the Press Pack. It was the text after the photograph. The first issue was the slogan. The Manager thought we needed to come up with a catchphrase that distinguished us from all the other wannabee bands trying to get a grip on the greasy showbiz pole. Something that encapsulated our sound and our attitude. So, we came up with this:

"ACM with balls!"

ACM being Adult Contemporary Music. To be honest, I have to take some responsibility for the slogan. I used my day job as a researcher to analyse trends in the music business—which revealed that ACM accounted for thirty-two per cent of the UK record market. The Manager and I decided we'd target this niche and splice on some value added with the proposition that we provided an additional hard edge to ACM.

The second issue was the part in the Press Pack entitled 'What are your ambitions for the future?'

That question is relevant if you're the Beatles doing an interview with Ed Sullivan after landing at Kennedy airport with three thousand screaming fans watching every rotation of the plane's front wheel as it trundles to its landing dock. The question is less relevant if you're doing a gig at a pub in Kingsbury.

But The Manager thought we needed to show we were a band that was going places. She decided it would be a good idea to demonstrate our ambitions by mixing bravado with irony. Each band member came up with a jokey sentence we thought would endear us to potential fans. My contribution was that the band aimed to extend its geographical operations to the provincial UK. Duff's immortal line was the band offered him an opportunity to make millions and retire early. We were smugly pleased with the press release. Then Harry Hazell stepped in.

Harry Hazell is the music critic of the Borehamwood Times. He runs a regular column called *Between the Grooves*. I'm in the middle of a particularly dysfunctional dream that combines faeces with winged angels and the carburetor of a vintage Sunbeam Alpine when the phone rings. It's The Manager. She sounds like she's hyperventilating.

"Have—youuu—seeen—the—Borehamwood—Times," she pants. I have to confess I haven't, on account of the fact I live in East London.

"It's a disaster," she says, managing to recover some semblance of breathing equilibrium.

"They've taken everything out of context. We look like a bunch of muppets."

She calls a band meeting for the following day. Turns up with photocopies of Harry Hazell's article.

This is what it says:

ACM with balls—that's how the seven piece jazz-funk collective describe themselves. Pretty sad really. Particularly when you discover ACM stands for adult contemporary music and the band's press release reveals this musical genre boasts a thirty-two per share of the record market. Frightening, isn't it? All those loaded thirty-somethings splashing out on anaemic drivel.

Apparently Level 42, Curiosity Killed the Cat and Joe Jackson are the class acts the band are compared to by their fans. But the icing on the cake is definitely the band's aim to "extend its geographical operations to the provincial UK." Do they mean gigging outside London?

Anyway, publicity material aside, the band dish up a mixture of jazz, Afro-Cuban and rock. The first track on the Victimised EP, Ordinary Madness, is something I'm sure world music mogul Andy Kershaw would savour. Reminiscent of just about any tune off Paul Simon's Graceland it bops along with piddly Bhundu Boys guitar arpeggios and staccato keyboard lines.

The band are accomplished musicians and the EP is slickly produced but they've got about as much balls as a eunuch's convention. Victimised is better, jazzier and more focused, while Come to My Rescue is a foray into piano-led ballad land—tinkly tosh. Keyboardist Duff Jones sees the band as an opportunity to make millions and retire early—dream on.

The band look like it's been hit by one of Cyrus's cymbals. Duff takes it, particularly to heart.

"Really sorry guys," he mumbles looking as sheepish as a flock of Shropshires. "I was just having a laugh with the making millions thing."

We nod sympathetically.

"I feel a right twat too," I offer supportively.

Duff looks even more crestfallen. We start to discuss damage limitation strategies. Maybe we should re-write the press release and send it back to Harry Hazell with an apology, saying he'd been given the first draft—the joke one—by mistake. Maybe we should take him out for a drink. Buy him a kebab. But as we discussed damage limitation, I sensed a shift in the band's mood. Why were we trying to ingratiate ourselves with some shit-kicker from the boonies? There were larger fish to fry in the big rock pool.

"Let's focus on high-value targets," said The Manager, sounding like the commander of a CIA black ops incursion—"like what Harry Hazell says—Andy Kershaw himself."

Suddenly, the band flipped from maudlin self-pity—you might call it victimised—to the Alex Ferguson siege mentality playbook. We decided to fight back.

We put together some rough outlines of posters, flyers and press releases for forthcoming gigs, starting with that evening's booking at The Swan.

BACK BY POPULAR DEMAND
Live at the Swan.
Funk jazz reggae soul.
'Unbeatable value' (Trolley Stop).
'I've seen more balls at a eunuch's convention' (Borehamwood Times).
SEE THE BAND HARRY HAZELL LOVES TO HATE
ADMISSION FREE! (concs; UB40's even more free).
Check out the extended play CD, available at the gig.

We're in the badlands of west London. The Swan. Fulham Broadway. I'm using the gig to road test Heart of England. It's a song I'd written trying to step into the shoes of Cyrus and Max. I'd imagined what it felt to be a kid in a mineral-rich country constantly exploited by multinationals and corrupt politicians. I tried to imagine how it felt to be in constant fear—the endless coups and savage violence dealt out to the population—all quietly endorsed by a colonial power sitting in London. The song has a reggae feel, 4/4. 130 BPM. It begins with an 8 bar vocal solo, without accompaniment:

Rain won't come
The ground's indifferent to your suffering
And the clay is hard as a banker's heart
Burning in the poisoned sun
Only shade the shadow of a gun
Soldiers smiling faces, guilty hands
Rich man's comfort from distant lands

Heart of England
wears its conscience on its sleeve.

Followed by an 8 bar bass and drum intro that builds up to boom into the first verse Dm, G:

digging in the earth
never see its worth
traded in the markets for arms and hard currency
democracy a travesty
get what you deserve
monuments to greed and repression and poverty

the chorus is Dm, Em, Dm, C

Diamonds are a politician's best friend
A seat on the board of a big corporation
Diamonds are a politician's best friend
Buy friends in high places and sell off the nation

Verse two is

Child can't cry
Brothers and sisters are taken at midnight
and no-one to tell them the reason why
letter from a charity
photographed place she'll never see
strangers smiling faces
and empty hands
images that she misunderstands
Heart of England
Promises you can't believe

An eight bar sax solo takes the song into a variation of the chorus

Diamonds are a politician's best friend
Resources sufficient to build anything

Diamonds are a politician's best friend
But the shares and the profits are pulling the strings

Then another chorus variation

Diamonds are a politician's best friend
Gifts to impress the ambassador's wife
Diamonds are a politician's best friend
Pay off the guards when you run for your life.

We slow the song down almost to a standstill in the finale. Four bars of silence followed by a single note on the Hammond

Young men dream
Green fields stretch into the future
And the waters shimmer against the sky
Endless possibility
Anything you want it can be
Take your freedom, cut the cord that ties
Soul of England
Beating still within the heart.

It turns out to be a tad over the top for the punters. The Swan has built its reputation on tribute bands and bands amalgamated from loose associations of bands. We're following in the footsteps of ReGenesis, with its recreation of the Genesis album *The Lamb lies down on Broadway*. There's *Paddy Goes to Hollyhead*, a melange of musicians with affiliations to Slade, Iron Maiden, Sweet, Mud and Whitesnake that range from deep to the width of a cigarette paper.

The punters are expecting to be comforted by a warm blanket of covers, not challenged by a revolutionary call to arms. The poignant last line of Heart of England is met with a wall of silence. I shift quickly into Temple of Love, reasoning that its pastiche of old Motown riffs will sound like a cover to the untutored ear. But it's too late. We've lost audience interest. As we finish the set a wave of relief breaks out.

The next day, I get a call from The Manager. She's very excited. A signal has been received from the Outer Reaches of the Music Universe. The first response to her mail shot. She's faxing it to me from the office. A few minutes later, my fax machine chirrups and spews out a couple of sheets.

I pick them up. It's hard to decipher what's written on them. The print is very faint. I haven't replaced the toner on the machine for years. I can just about make out that the document is from an outfit called LNT. It starts off with a gush about how thrilled LNT is to be given the opportunity to represent such promising artists as us. Then it dives into a forest of legalese so dense I feel the need to lie down in a darkened room. Eventually, it grinds to a conclusion.

In its capacity as an employment agency, LNT is neither an artiste nor an employer. It generally arranges engagements between the two parties thus forming contracts between the artiste and employers.

The distribution of artistes/agents publicity material and business cards which include any telephone numbers other than the LNT number is specifically FORBIDDEN at any venue at which the artiste has been booked by LNT. If the artiste accepts any re-engagement with the employer/venue within twelve calendar months from the completion of the original engagement the artiste must inform LNT office WITHIN 48 hours.

In any event, any re-engagement with the employer/venue shall be deemed to have been negotiated through LNT and be subject to the SAME commission or charge if re-engagement is made within twelve calendar months from the completion of the original engagement. LNT Terms and Conditions apply to all re-engagements referred to herein.

It gives us great pleasure to add your act to our books and we will do everything we can to secure work for you in the very near future.

Rock and roll. We appear to be now owned by LNT. All we need to do is sit back, relax and wait for the gigs to come streaming in.

I started to see Geordie Burn and Kinmont Willie through the lens of extended phenotyping. It was obvious the Reivers were survival machines that developed genes for plundering and pillaging as an adaptive response to a harsh environment. Just as the caddis fly developed genes for selecting valuable crap from a river bed, so Geordie and Willie had developed genes for raping and stabbing. I considered the historical evidence. Books devoted to the Reivers contained frequent references to what I believed to be phenotyping.

"Reiving was the only way to survive—the practice spread and was passed down through generations—it produced a fine independent people with strong qualities of resilience and resolution—it produced the Borderers, with their many descendants scattered throughout the world still displaying those notable characteristics acquired through those eventful and bloody years."

It was obvious to me that reiving was a textbook paradoxical evolutionary stable strategy—a study in stuckness. On the one hand, Reivers displayed fine qualities of resilience and adaptation to a harsh and unforgiving environment— as any good survival machine does.

But on the other, like some 17th century dinosaurs, they displayed behavioural strategies that were unreconstructed and unsustainable. Acts of courage and loyalty went hand in hand with deceit and treachery. People on the outside—usually the victims—viewed Reivers through an ambivalent lens of attraction and repulsion. Non-reivers were romanced by the glamour and myth.

But, if you were a citizen, you wouldn't want your daughter to be romanced by a Reiver. Citizens feared the midnight raid; the kidnapping and the ransom; the incipient recklessness of it all; the uncertainty and turbulence that went with the territory. The law-abiding recognised the need to adapt to changing times. The act of Union that joined together England and Scotland imposed power and control on the Border Region, requiring citizens to subordinate themselves to the new order.

But it also offered new opportunities for peace and prosperity. Reivers couldn't adapt to these changing economic and social conditions. Like the outlaws of the American Wild West—whose numbers included their direct descendants—and the brothers of the Sicilian Cosa Nostra who superseded them, the Border Reivers were prisoners of their survival strategy.

What happened to the Reivers following the Act of Union confirmed my suspicion that they were operating a fatally flawed ESS. Once England and Scotland were united in 1603, James I made a determined effort to off the Reivers. He was motivated not least by a brazen display of reiving that took advantage of the power vacuum created between the death of Elizabeth I and James' coronation.

During this hiatus, subsequently called 'Ill Week', several Scottish reiving families launched full-on raids into Cumbria, deploying the ingenious pretext of a custom claiming that when a monarch died the laws of the land were automatically suspended until the new king was crowned.

Considerably put out at the ensuing loss of 1,280 cattle and 3,840 sheep and goats following the raid, James I issued a decree against 'all rebels and disorderly persons'. This abolished Border Law—and the very idea of the 'Borders' itself. The old border areas—the 'Marches'—were renamed the 'Middle Shires'. In 1605 James established a commission to bring law and order to the region. In the first year of the commission's existence, it executed 79 Reivers. Other Reivers fled with their families to the 'Ulster Plantation' of Northern Ireland.

The Ulster Plantation is a deceptively lyrical term for the enforced colonisation of the North of Ireland by Great Britain. Like the Scottish Borders, Ulster had been the most difficult part of Ireland to control. Like the Borders, it was underpopulated and underdeveloped, mainly because it too was difficult to farm. And, like the Borders, its social and cultural fabric was dominated by close-knit clans.

Directly preceded by the Nine Years War in the 1590s, the Plantation, according to historians, continued the attempt by the English crown to break the power of the clan chiefs in the North of Ireland. The historian W Leckey describes the war as 'literally a war of extermination'. The native population were 'crushed to the dust' and the 'complete ascendancy of English law' in Ireland was established.

Another historian, George O'Brien saw it as a situation where the 'popular land system was finally abolished' and the Irish people reduced to a condition 'not far removed from slavery'. They argue that although Queen Elizabeth I had no real interest in conquering Ulster, its under-development aroused the interest of British elites, as British elites have always been aroused throughout history by the prospect of a quick buck at the expense of the natives. Following the succession of James I, the 'Plantation' was hawked to the King in a power-point presentation as a joint British venture to 'pacify and civilise Ulster'.

As a result, rich and powerful cliques like the 'Undertakers'—wealthy English and Scottish Landowners—and the Livery companies and Guilds in London—saw opportunities to make them even richer and more powerful. The plan stipulated that at least half the settlers would be Scots. The main landowners were to be the key investors in the venture—the Undertakers, Livery companies and Guilds, who were granted around 3000 acres each, on condition that they settle a minimum of 48 adult males, who had to be English-speaking and Protestant.

These settlers were supplemented by Servitors—officer veterans of the Nine Years War, who were subsidised by the London guilds. A large number of settlers were Border Reivers. Part of the logic of the Plantation plan was that moving Borderers to Ireland would solve the Border problem and pacify Ulster. James VI of Scotland was particularly keen to offload the Reiver families to Ulster, since, when he became King of England too he knew his job would be made much harder if the Reivers were still raping and pillaging.

As Travers Cosgrove—a twenty-first-century descendant of William Armstrong—saw it:

"James made it clear he wanted no more border incursions 'for the fun of it'. So he removed several Scots border clans and 'planted' them to settle in northern Ireland—in Ulster. He had inherited trouble here and thought to cure it this way. And so the border clans arrived as Presbyterians in a country where the majority of the inhabitants were Roman Catholic and the administration, Anglican."

You could think of this Reiver exodus via the 'Plantation Plan', as a transplantation to Ulster of the old 'intruder wins' strategy that had been such a dominant feature of the Reivers way of life in the Scottish Borders. Marginalised economically and culturally in their own habitat, the Reivers had mounted their own kind of scorched earth campaign against residents and authority alike.

Beaten finally by an ascendant State, they were rounded up and moved on so they could continue being intruders elsewhere. But what happened in Ulster shows that the paradoxical strategy that failed the Reivers in the Borders also failed them in their new habitat. The history of the Reivers following the implementation of the Ulster Plantation Plan is a continuation of their previous, paradoxical narrative—resilience and courage; fear and loathing; murder and arson—and further displacement.

From 1609 onwards, the Borderers settled in Ulster either through being recruited by Undertakers to their estates or through migrating themselves to unpopulated areas. Some Borderers were not best pleased with the grotty land they were assigned and moved elsewhere in Ireland. The land issue was a particular problem for the new arrivals. Most settled on uninhabited and unexploited land, often building their farms and homes in woods and bogs. The new Plantation settlers didn't displace the indigenous Irish, except in heavily populated areas like Armagh.

According to Marianne Elliot, "By the 1630s, evidence suggests that the plantation was settling down—There was tacit religious tolerance and in every county, Old Irish were serving as royal officials and members of the Irish Parliament."

Yet, you can take Reivers out of the Border, but you can't take the Border out of the Reiver. As time went on, the old reiving ways re-surfaced. The new frontier began to experience a plague of rustling and pillaging, with former soldiers of the Gaelic lords joining with renegades from the new immigrants to rob and murder Protestants and Catholics alike. In reaction, in 1609, Chichester, the Lord Deputy, deported 1,300 former Irish soldiers to Sweden to serve in the army. This relatively low scale lairyness was, however, a prelude to the large-scale mayhem that occurred from 1630 onwards.

In the 1630s, Presbyterians in Scotland rebelled against Charles the First's attempt to install Anglican god-botherers in a country used to a more austere form of god-bothering. The Scottish settlers in Ulster saw a good opportunity for a ruck and a large number of them went back to Scotland to support the rebellion. Charles, I hit on the idea of recruiting an army composed entirely of Irish Catholics and sent them to Ulster to prepare to invade Scotland.

Meanwhile, Gaelic Irish landowners in Ulster planned a rebellion to take over the administration in Ireland. In 1641, the Catholic army turned on the British colonists, massacring about 4000 and booting out 12,000 more. As the historian, Marianne Elliott puts it "1641 destroyed the Ulster Plantation as a mixed settlement."

Many historians believe the massacres had a lasting impact on the Ulster Protestant population. A.T.Q. Stewart says, "The fear which it inspired survives in the Protestant subconscious as the memory of the Penal Laws or the Famine persists in the Catholic—Here, if anywhere, the mentality of siege was born, as the warning bonfires blazed from hilltop to hilltop and the beating drums summoned men to the defence of castles and walled towns crowded with refugees."

Wille Armstrong's descendant, Travers Cosgrove, sees it this way:

"Almost four centuries later, things are still much the same and this fear of being overwhelmed persists. So, the Scots Armstrong were an early example of 'Social Engineering'! Their presence was resented by the locals; their educational and religious culture feared and frowned upon by the authorities; their social and family units probably broken up—perhaps because they didn't correspond with the available land and too many in one place would be too powerful."

In 1642, the Scottish Parliament sent 10,000 soldiers to put down the Irish rebellion. In revenge for the massacres of the Scottish colonists, the army did what most armies do when supporting a colonial power and went in hard against the Catholic population. In retaliation, the colonists around Derry and east Donegal got together to organise the Laggan Army.

As ever, it was the civilians who suffered, as all sides massacred the innocent, further escalating the population displacement begun by the Plantation. As well as fighting the Ulster Irish, the British settlers fought each other between 1648 and 1649 in a side-show to the English Civil War over the water. The Scottish Presbyterian army sided with the King and the Laggan Army sided with the English Parliament.

From 1649 to 1650, Cromwell's New Model Army hammered both the Scottish forces and the Ulster Irish. Again, the Borderers were on the losing side and lost power and land after the re-colonisation of Ireland by Cromwell. Yet again, the Reivers found themselves on the wrong side of progress. By the middle of the eighteenth century, thousands of Border Reiver descendants had emigrated to the American colonies. Some of them fought in the War of Independence. Others set sail for Australia, New Zealand and Canada.

It seems my own branch of the clan didn't go long-haul. On looking at the evidence, it's possible they went back to the Borders. The records suggest that my grandmother's family came from the Gaelic clan MacThrenfeir. They originated in County Clare, in southwest Ireland. And they were associated with the Armstrong family—the infamous clan of Kinmont Willie.

Tracing your lineage is fraught with problems. Haplotyping work on Reivers shows we are a mix of Spanish Basques, Celtic Brits, Angles, Saxons and Jutes and Danish Vikings. We're also descended from Neolithic tribes in Central Asia, brought to Britain by Phonecian traders and Roman troops.

And then there are the social and cultural factors. The turmoil of daily life in the Borders meant your father might go out on a moonlight raid one night and turn up dead the next morning. Bereaved sons of dead Reivers were often adopted by another family. Border families encouraged trial marriages and allowed wives to keep their maiden names. The clans themselves were also political animals and many men adopted the surnames of other clans for protection.

In addition, much of the genealogy of the Reivers was scrambled when they were forced to resettle in Ulster. Yet, despite all this mash-up, the evidence suggests it's more than possible that a little of the blood of Kinmont Willie ran through my veins.

I turned my attention to the other branch of my ancestors—the paternal line. My parental ancestry is Irish Catholic, from the Gaelic clan MacCuillin, who came from Gleann Cuilinn, County Wicklow, just south of Dublin, on the Kildare-Wicklow border. One source suggested I was descended from an acolyte of Strongbow—the warlord not the cider. Strongbow was Richard fitz Gilbert de Clare, Earl of Pembroke, named thus for his skill and use of the long bow.

He was pimped by Dermot MacMurchada Lord of Leinster in 1168 to marry Leinster's daughter, Eve. On settling into Ireland, Strongbow proved himself useful to Henry II, King of England, by helping the king put down a rebellion by Irish Lords. In recognition of his services, Strongbow was given a shed-load of land and a title.

Whatever the origin, my paternal line, according to the DNA project run by a contemporary ancestor in Seattle, USA shows that my family was concentrated in Dublin, Wicklow and Wexford. However, other records bring back the spectre of the Borderers. One source makes a connection between my paternal family and a Gaelic Captain, who is said to have arrived in Ireland with Cromwell in 1648 and founded the family in County Leitrim.

So, whichever side of the lineage I looked at, in both parental lines, we had criss-crossed the Irish Sea. Both lines had ended up in Ireland, the Armstrong connection possibly arriving a little late on into *phytophthora infestans*. The fallout from the potato blight and subsequent Great Famine of 1845 has been well documented. Approximately one million of the population died.

A similar number took their chances on overcrowded ships for an uncertain future elsewhere. My family took the shortest route to a new future—one hundred and thirty-four miles across the Irish Sea to Merseyside. My own survival machine had landed in Liverpool. But did it carry the Reiver's genes?

May

Wake up. Go to the bathroom. Look in the mirror. Don't look down. Look down. Oh, Horror. The MPB has got worse. It seems to have proliferated to form a scrubland the size of a small principality. Resolve to explore opportunities to restore scalp to its former lustre. After breakfast, I peruse adverts on hair transplantation.

- Achieving full, natural results can give back the confidence you've lost and take your confidence to new heights.
- Invest in your hair.
- It's the crown you never take off.

I've got two choices. First—the Strip Method. A thin strip of skin with my hair clinging to it is removed from the back of my head and divided into pieces. The grafts are placed into tiny cuts made in my scalp. The sites they took my hair from are stitched up. There's a scar on the back of my head.

Second—the Follicular Unit Extraction Method. The back of my head is shaved. Individual hair grafts are removed from my scalp. They put tiny cuts in my scalp and insert the grafts. I end up with a carpet of tiny scars. Either way, it all looks very painful. Further analysis reveals shocking tariffs for the treatment in Harley Street so I broaden my horizons and settle on a clinic in Wakefield that's half the price.

Chuffing North to Wakefield on the old LNER line each mile bringing me closer to an encounter with the scalpel. As we speed through the decaying heartlands of old Albion a Genesis song 'Selling England by the Pound' pops into my head. I use the time to work on an idea for a song called 'Desperate, lonely, suicidal?'

It speaks to friendless no-marks in grey bed-sits. Probationary teachers longing to wear leiderhosen in the classroom. Wannabe models stacking Tesco shelves, aching to fork out a month's pay for a professional glamour shoot. It's a call to arms for anyone who's ever thought they could do better than they're doing now. It's an anti-stuckness manifesto.

Arrive at Wakefield Central. A taxi takes me to the Wakefield Transplant Centre. It's located in an industrial estate at the edge of town next to a car breakers yard. The reception area looks and feels like the Job Centre I last visited a decade ago. Skid-marked seats. Well-thumbed copies of Homes and Gardens.

There's a fish tank in the corner to soothe punters' anxieties about the Strip Method. I wander over to it and make eye contact with a guppy. It wins the ensuing stare out competition. I hear the clunk of an opening door latch, turn around and there stands Dr Adrian Metcalfe, MB ChB, FRCS, BAHRS—fully qualified member of the British Association of Hair Restoration Surgery. He's dressed in an Armani suit and flashes me a smile that illuminates two matching tiers of expensive orthodontics. He looks about fourteen.

The Strip Method is every bit as traumatic as I'd anticipated, despite the administration of a local anaesthetic. Adrian's chair-side manner is like an extremely hard-core version of the conversation you have at the hairdresser. Have you got any plans for the holidays he asks as a precision steel medical instrument slices through the skin on the back of my skull. I feel the hairs on the back of my neck stand up in empathy.

I'm struggling to string together a response. Not yet I mutter as the scalpel extracts another slice of flesh from the back of my head. Bear in mind he says as he cuts off another strip. You need to be careful with the sun. Try not to expose the graft or the extraction site to too much ultra-violet. Or you might get an ultra-violent reaction he sniggers. I'll be going to Greenland I reply. Never been there says Adrian. Has it got good beaches?

Back on the LNER to Kings Cross. The scalp is really painful. I'm getting recurrent headaches. The grafts are constantly itching and I'm desperate to scratch them. The itching is exacerbated by the fez-kufi I feel obliged to wear to camouflage the transplant. The Manager is waiting for me at the station in the clapped-out Astra. She takes me home. My home.

The morning after, we're in in the middle of an act of mutually degrading copulation when Bill phones me. It's a welcome interruption. There's other things we'd be better off doing somewhere else—like waterboarding the music critic from the Borehamwood Gazette. Bill mistakes my slightly breathless greeting for excitement at the chance for the band to demean itself by playing in front of a bunch of semi-comatose tourists at the Rock Garden that evening. The band he's signed up have pulled out at short notice. Could we step into the breach?

I quickly accept the invitation. Too quickly. But he knows I know there's scores of other bands in his Filofax waiting for the call. I cut the connection. Roll back onto the mattress, the viscoelastic cells of the memory-foam forming a deep depression into which I sink, echoing my mood. The Manager props herself on one elbow, her face creasing into that unmistakable grin I know too well—that salivating, predatory gig grin.

I do a band ring round. Some of them are not happy at the short notice—you know who they are. But the Rock Garden is a showcase venue. Right smack in the middle of Covent Garden. Big tourist pull. They agree to turn up—albeit reluctantly. I arrive for the sound check in grey half-light, the point of time when Soho disgorges its late lunch stragglers and prepares itself for the evening onslaught. It was already dark when the band finally converged, transitioning from various points of the compass.

Pete turns up on his old ramshackle cycle, guitar strapped around his neck like a noose. Max emerges from the Underground like the Commendatore in Don Giovanni. Flimsy arrives in an entourage of four wheel drives, like the head of a Colombian cartel. Cyrus pulls up in a taxi, his extravagant ensemble of percussion extracted from the boot like so many hat boxes. We manhandle the gear down the rickety stairs to the basement, our footwear adhering at each step to the glutinous residue of the previous evening's jurgemeisters.

Despite the balmy temperature outside, the air in the basement is almost freezing. The uncladded walls ooze moisture. It collects in puddles on the floor.

Cyrus begins to set up his drum-kit on the cramped stage. He always seems to take a lifetime. Each piece is carefully extracted from its protective cocoon. Each item is meticulously reassembled. Then the separate items are painstakingly merged together to form a coherent whole. Cyrus eases himself down onto his tiny stool and subjects each part of the assembly to a vigorous interrogation. The bass drum thumped—the snare rapped—the high hat tamped within an inch of its life.

Brendan extracts the Fender from its battered case, covered with peeling stickers—Atomkraft? Neine, Danke!—plugs it into the amp. Connects the amp to a weeping socket. The band launches jerkily into Cantaloupe. I'm not involved in the prep, so I watch how the band is performing. Brendan looks more energised than usual. Head nodding rhythmically to the 4/4 beat, feet stomping in time.

He's gripping the bass strings as if they're lifelines, grinning like a gopher. It's like he's welded to the strings. The amplifier's emitting a discordant drone, like the sound of a car alarm. And I notice there's a tiny cluster of sparks arcing up from where the lead from the guitar feeds into the amplifier. Realise that the Rock Garden basement is so saturated with moisture it's like one big amorphous circuit—the moisture has connected the guitar to the amplifier to Brendan.

Realises he's in an advanced phase of electrocution. He's rocking backwards and forwards on his heels, teeth bared like a Death Row inmate strapped to Old Smokey. I vacillate between self-preservation and the inconvenience of having to find a bass player at short notice.

Absolving me from the trauma of decision, the ever-practical Pete steps into the breach. Hands insulated with a pair of improvised oven gloves hastily assembled from the stage curtains he separates Brendan from his lethal embrace with the guitar and unplugs the amp. A diminutive cloud of smoke rises from the guitar and mingles with the overhanging fug of the basement.

"Fuck me, bruv," says Max, extricating a spliff from his sax case. "I thought you was a goner there."

Flimsy moves in close and showers Brendan with solicitous kisses, whilst patting him down like a reception officer at Pentonville prison. Max looks a tad put out. Brendan looks grateful. Then his legs give way and he slumps slo-mo to the floor as if tidily folding himself in preparation for bed. Flimsy darts in to give him mouth-to-mouth resuscitation. Max looks even more put out. But Brendan waves her away.

"I'm OK," he says, just a bit winded.

We move back to give him some space. After a few minutes, he gets to his feet. Smiles. "That was weird," he says, then goes to pick up his bass.

Pete puts out an arm to bar his path. The Manager goes upstairs to see the Venue Manager. The Venue Manager sends an electrician down to check the circuits. After twenty minutes of prodding and probing, he delivers his verdict. Everything's fine. There's nothing shorting. Pete's not convinced.

"So, how come our bass player's just been fried," he asks.

The electrician shrugs. "One of those things," he says. "Unfortunate coincidence. Must have been some water dripped onto the lead. Million to one."

I ask Brendan if he's OK to carry on.

He smiles. "Rock and Roll," he says.

We complete the sound check with no further drama. Go outside to the square and have a drink in a neighbouring pub to calm us all down. When we get back, the manager and I take a quick peek at the guest list that's kept at the box office. Speed-scan the names. It's the usual hangers on. But then two names leap out. I've never heard of them. But it's the affiliation that grabs my attention.

In the category marked 'organisation' is the moniker of a well-known record company. We're being scouted! We take the decision to withhold the information from band colleagues. Additional excitement on top of a near electrocution would almost certainly destabilise the band to the detriment of their operational efficiency. We leave instructions with the box office to provide the record company representatives with whatever refreshment they need. The tab is on the band.

We go downstairs. The Garden is mobbed. There must be two hundred people crammed in there. I reckon half of them are Flimsy's entourage. Looks like her entire extended family is on the dance floor. I recognise her dad and the uncles, surrounded by the Essex mafia. I'm thinking that's a good result because we only get paid for tickets sold beforehand.

I go on stage wearing the fez. My usual robotic movements are even more restrained for fear of it coming off and exposing the gory topography of the transplant. A couple of numbers into the first set I notice Flimsy's dad and one of the uncles making their way determinedly towards the sound engineer's booth in the centre of the dance floor. I'm trying to concentrate on my performance but my eye can't help being drawn to what's happening near the booth.

I see words exchanged between the engineer and the dad. The uncle appears to be making a point—the point emphasised by a stabbing gesture of his right hand. Then the dad and uncle retire back to the dance floor. And suddenly the whole balance of the band sound changes. Flimsy's backing vocals get much louder. They're transformed into lead vocals. I'm struggling to be heard. Fuck me. Her dad and uncle have strong-armed the sound engineer. He's turned me down and turned her up.

I simmer through the rest of the numbers as we head towards the interval, trying to focus, but all the time images of punishment and retribution pop into my head. Flimsy in a dungeon, shackled to restraining bars, starving, dehydrated, a plate of food and a bowl of water placed just out of reach. Flimsy teetering precariously on the gangplank as voracious sharks circle below. Flimsy roped to the track as the locomotive hurtles inexorably towards her.

Finally, we reach the halfway point of the set. As I walk off stage, I see the Essex Mafia encircling her. She absorbs the adulation like an imperial empress.

Whilst they're preoccupied I sidle up to the sound engineer. He looks nervous at my approach.

"What's your name?" I ask as I intrude on his space.

"Edmund," he replies.

"Well, Edmund, I'm sure you know Newton's third law of motion."

He looks puzzled.

"It goes like this. To every action, there's an equal and opposite reaction. Meaning, you were leaned on by the backing singer's posse. So, you turned her volume up to a point where I was completely drowned out. My equal and opposite reaction is I need her volume turned down so it does what it's supposed to do—back the lead singer. If you don't restore the levels to what they were at the sound check, I'll come back when we've finished the set and stick your mixing desk up your arse. Capiche?"

"OK," he nods. "Fair enough." Walking back to the stage I clock two blokes standing near the stairs. They're wearing suits and holding pint glasses filled to the brim. As I pass they smile and raise their glasses. Thank you, God! Must be the A&R guys from the record company. I grin back inanely.

We start the second half with Dirty Linen. It's a pared down song. Latin feel. Drums quietly following the melody in the background. Guitar is almost acoustic. No pyrotechnics until we build up to the outro. It gives me a lot of space and time to own the vocal. Flimsy doesn't get an opportunity until we're three verses in, then she gives it the harmony on the chorus. So she's unprepared for what happens when we get there. I almost burst out laughing when she launches into the chorus.

Her face is a picture of baffled incomprehension as she belts it out and it comes back through the monitors like a damp firework. Her eyes swivel towards the sound engineer's booth, dagger him straight to the heart. But he's ducked down behind the mixing desk. Then they swivel towards me but I'm already beyond their reach. I've moved right to the edge of the stage, almost leaning into the audience and I'm cradling the mic as if it's a long-lost lover, washing myself in the wonderful me-sound that's swooning out through the Rock Garden's speaker stack.

From there on things go to plan. My plan. We finish the set with a rousing rendition of Temple of Love. Here, it is in all its cod Motown glory.

Ridiculous tempo—120 BPM. 4/4 time. Starts with a classic Motown eight bar drum and sax intro—just two notes repeated Dm7, G7. Then I come in with the first verse, same chords:

I can't believe what's happened to me
I'm a prisoner and I can't break free
The chains are heavy and the jailor's stealin' my life away
I got religion and my soul's on fire
burnin' in the flame of desire
I'm carrying a torch for a high priestess and I can't let go

Verse two switches to F sharp 7, then G7

Court of appeal can do nothing for me
The door is open but I can't break free
I'll forfeit all of my days and nights for an hour with you

then we steam into the chorus

I'm a slave in the Temple of Love (repeat X4).

then back to verse 1 structure

I get so restless I can't sleep any more
went to the doctor say now give me a cure
consulted all of the medical books to see what's wrong with me
he says it baffles the practitioner's mind
a diagnosis is so hard to find
there's no prescription for your problem that can see you through.

We repeat the chorus then the middle eight suspends the song in space, anchored by Cyrus's drums and the return of the clanky rhythm guitar chords as we scaffold the finale in Am7:

there's no solution
no absolution
no emancipation
no quick salvation
all thoughts behind me
that's where you'll find me
sacrificed on the altar of love
finishing with a circuit of repeated choruses
I'm a slave in the Temple of Love.

The crowd are well into the vibe. They're jumping up and down as the cod soul sounds reverberate around the dank basement. I can see the A&R men, still in their corner, smiling and raising glasses that are magically again full to the brim. As usual, I introduce the band, giving them each eight bars to make their mark. I savour what might look like the intentional slight of leaving Flimsy until last.

Give it up for that belle of backing singers—Miss Flimsy Wipers—I trumpet. She's not looking the happiest of backing singers but gives it her best. Scire cum victus es. Know when the tables are turned. All in all, a great night. Brendan clutched from the jaws of death. Flimsy's plan to send me to sound oblivion thwarted. The band deliver a top performance witnessed by A&R men from a top record company.

During the second half of the set, The Manager had taken it upon herself to approach the A&R's and ask them for contact details. Now, as we're standing in a near-deserted Rock Garden, she gets a brain-wave. You need to strike when the iron's hot, she says and calls one of them. The dial tone cuts out abruptly. Wrong number. She tries the other number. The same thing happens. We go back upstairs to see if they've left any contact details so we can check the numbers. We explain to the box office receptionist what we want. Her face creases up.

"Oh, dear," she says. "Imposter syndrome."

The Manager and I exchange blank looks.

"Happens all the time," the receptionist says. "We get a lot of chancers turning up and signing the guest list as record company reps. They drink shitloads of free booze then bugger off, leaving the band with the bill. You didn't invite them, then," she says looking a tad smug.

"Unfortunately not," I reply.

"Oh, dear. Here's the bar bill," she says sliding a piece of paper the size of the Magna Carta across the counter. "The bill comes to just under fifty quid. And here's your fee statement," she says sliding another piece of paper across the counter.

I scrutinise the figures. There were over 200 people at the gig. But we only get paid for the punters we directly sell tickets to. That's 42 people. We get 10% of the admission fee. That's 42 quid. Less the bar bill. We've just made minus 8 quid for playing our guts out in one of London's major tourist attractions.

The next day The Manager calls me. She's received another response to the mail-shot. She faxes it. This is what it says:

Thank you for your enquiry. Have you ever asked yourself why it is that some writers, even those with less than average ability, seem to get all the breaks while others, even those with immense talent, never seem to go anywhere?

Then let me introduce you to THE INTERNATIONAL SONGWRITER—the powerful new manual that shows you step by step how you can achieve any target you set yourself as a songwriter.

<u>This manual will show you:</u>

How to make all the contacts you need and reach the people that matter.

How to demo your songs without spending a fortune.

How to get international artists to record your songs.

P.S. THE INTERNATIONAL SONGWRITER *is printed on high gloss paper with a strong A4 laminated cover to last a lifetime.*

"What do you think?" she says. "Should we get back to them?"

"You really don't want to know what I think," I reply. "Has there been anything from LNT?"

She responds with a negative.

"I'll be round your place at seven," I say and cut the connection. Resist the temptation to scratch the still suppurating scalp.

My dad's been doing the Houses of Parliament for months. It's the culmination of his un-retirement. Ever since he got retired he'd been applying all his energies to getting unretired. All his life his existence had been defined by employment. By being *Sinbad the Sailor*.

I remember one time when my mother had reached the end of her tether after twenty years left to fend for five kids on her own. She gave him an ultimatum. Pack in the sailoring and get a shore job. There was no 'or else'. The 'else' was silently but deafeningly expressed in the ultimatum. So, he packed the sailoring in and got a maintenance job in a dog food factory. It was a bad choice all around.

Each day my father rose at 6 AM and got the bus to St Helens. He'd spend eight hours maintaining machinery that was perfectly all right on its own. At the end of the shift, he'd get the bus back and arrive at the house in a mood. We'd sit at the dinner table enveloped in a grump cloud, hoping it wouldn't escalate. The only perk of the job was the free pet food. The only pet we had was an African Grey my dad had smuggled back from Nigeria. Despite prolonged coaxing, the parrot preferred its peanuts. It was only a matter of time before all parties in the household—especially the parrot—wished him back at sea.

It was with great relief to all that after a month at the dog food factory he announced he'd accepted an offer to sail to the Caribbean in a banana boat as Chief Engineer. In subsequent years, he never set foot on dry land except for shore leave. Until now. The problem with shore leave for my father my was that it was the opposite of what it was meant to be. Instead of a welcome respite from the toils and tribulations of life on the ocean wave, a chance to recharge the batteries, returning to Blighty meant an intimidating immersion in the unfamiliar.

When he came back for a few weeks off after a yearlong trip to Nigeria or Saudi Arabia, he didn't know what to do with himself. The initial few days were easy. Clock off. Down the gangway. Down to Yates' Wine Lodge. The unsteady trek home. Re-learning how to communicate with the family. Failing dismally to communicate with the family. Yates' Wine Lodge. The unsteady trek home. As the enforced idleness ground on, he'd develop an increasingly severe case of shore-itis—a chronic aversion to buildings, lawns and domestic responsibility.

The problem with retirement was that it was permanent shore leave. There were a few pluses. One bonus was that the kids had all left home. Another was the normalisation of drink. He could go to the pub on a regular basis and sink a regular few pints instead of necking vast quantities of beer and rum every time he came down the gangway.

He was headhunted for a Pub Quiz team, on account of his gift for fact-retention and unparalleled expertise in the specialist subjects of 60s musicals and the history of Liverpool FC. But the downside of retirement was it never ended. Before he'd been retired he could sketch in his mind's eye that point in time when he'd pack his carry-all, go down the stairs, submit himself to farewell fumblings then close the door and leave it all behind.

Post-retirement, all he could see in his mind's eye was an arid vista of inconsequentiality—a road along which his empty shell, made meaningless through lack of purpose, plodded towards its inevitable oblivion.

That's why he turned up at my door, well into his seventies. One of his mates on the Pub Quiz team—the boss of an engineering firm—had blagged a contract to re-fit the boilers in the Houses of Parliament. He'd assembled a crew and invited my dad to join it. Reading between the lines I get the impression the invitation is part hard-nosed business and part charity. The boss knows my father has earned his stripes as an engineer and has a reputation as someone who knows his stuff, works hard and gets the job done.

At the same time, he's clocked up a fair few years in the wilderness and he's not as strong as he used to be, bearing in mind the Parliament job is strenuous physical graft. But the boss also knows my father is worth his weight in platinum as a romancer, a laugh-maker, a storyteller. So, he gets a berth on the Parliament Express.

Each day he gets picked up from my house in the scally-mobile. One of the privileges of being a Houses of Parliament contractor is that you don't have to take public transport like the mortals. You can drive the scally-mobile straight into the Parliament car-park. The scally-mobile is driven by Declan. He's from Huyton—the same shit-hole Steven Gerrard came from. Declan is covered in so many tattoos he makes the Illustrated Man look like a Robert Ryman painting.

In addition to Declan, the scally-mobile is crammed with an assorted crew of brickies, chippies, sparkies and ex-mariners. For me, it's a far stretch from being a time-served marine engineer with over five decades of experience hammering a diesel engine into submission in a force ten gale off the Cape of Good Hope to replacing the boilers that keep the bunch of donkeys who lead us warm enough to maintain their viability but prevent them dozing off. But to my dad it's salvation.

He's especially pleased with his Parliamentary Visitors Pass. After all these years of being stereotyped as a scally, he feels he's been elevated to the top table.

Stereotyped or not, he's already scally-tongued the security staff to the extent that they're on first name terms.

If he were a real terrorist—as opposed to terrorising me in my formative years—he'd have no trouble smuggling a six megaton nuclear device into the Chambers. I'm not sure exactly what he does in those hours after he leaves the house heading for the mother of all Parliaments. He doesn't go into the specifics much. But when the scally-mobile drops him off at the end of the day he's so exhausted he can hardly make it down the pathway.

The doorbell rings. He's forgotten his key again. I open the door and he's standing there in his work clothes showering what could be a lethal dose of asbestos fibre all over the hallway. He's brandishing something in his hand.

"I got you a pressie," he says stepping over the threshold and wiping his feet on the doormat, funnelling another cloud of radioactive asbestos into the interior of the house. He hands over the object. I peer closely. It's a key ring. The round metallic O of the ring is attached to a green leather grip, embossed with a gold portcullis. I don't know what to say. It's the first gift he's ever given me in person. I don't know how to respond.

"Thanks," I say, "it'll come in handy."

I've made us dinner. It's a starter of whitebait, delicately floured and deep-fried in sesame oil. Followed by braised rabbit with rosemary. My father looks at the starter dubiously. He forks a mouthful of whitebait and chews gingerly as if masticating steel wool. I ask if he's happy with the starter. He grimaces.

"Oh, aye, it's great," he says plucking the spine of a whitebait from between his teeth.

"It tastes like the salt fish we used to get at sea."

I pour him another glass of the vintage Douro I got on special offer from Majestic.

"Nice drink," he says "really helps to wash it down."

As we get into the wine the tales start to flow. He tells me about the time he's working in Nigeria for a company that works for a bigger company that drills for oil. His own company dredges the river so the bigger company can install its test rigs. They employ local people to do things like stoke the boilers on the dredger, bring in supplies, cook for the crew. My dad's stuck in the middle of nowhere. He's bored senseless. So he decides to form a Nose-Band.

It's a ridiculously simple concept. There are no musical instruments to hand. So you make an instrument out of your own nose. He assembles all the locals and assigns each one a position in each of the sections in the Nose-Band. There's a brass section, a wind section, a strings section and a percussion section. For each section, there's a particular nose-technique you need to learn so the sounds that come out of the nasal passages are as close an approximation as you can get to the sounds that emerge from a real instrument.

His aim—the Nose-band Village Concert. He sets up a practice session every Wednesday, late in the afternoon when the heat is less brutal, so each member of the band is singing from the same nose-sheet. He drills them into learning the concert repertoire. The concert features five nose-songs each taken from his favourite musicals:

I'm gonna wash that man right out of my hair (South Pacific).

What do the simple folk do (Camelot)?

America (West Side Story).

The surrey with the fringe on top (Oklahoma).

And the piece de resistance—You'll never walk alone (Carousel).

As he's describing the scene where the Nose-Band launches into the Village Concert Overture he clocks my expression of disbelief.

"Honest to God," he says. "They all turned up on the Sunday dressed up. White shirts. Bow ties. The village Headman's in the front row. There was two hundred in the audience. We did six encores. I'll show you."

He goes upstairs to his bedroom and brings down an old leather briefcase. Opens it up. Rummages through the contents and pulls out a faded black and white photograph. And there it is. The Nigerian Nose Band. All dressed in their Sunday best. All assembled in regimented rows like the Philharmonic Orchestra. I have to laugh. It's so comical.

My father's in a groove. He's surfing on stories. We're back in the Nigerian Delta. The oil company has got permission to drill in the interior. But there's a problem. One of the sites is a burial ground. The local Headman tells the company it's taboo to drill on the site. There's a warning of dire consequences. But money talks. The drilling goes ahead.

My dad comes down to the engine room on the dredger one afternoon. It's over forty degrees centigrade down there. You can hardly breathe for the heat. And in a corner, he finds one of the local employees. Shivering. He's wearing a big woollen overcoat. But he's shivering. He can't speak. He can't move. They get him out of the dredger and drive him to a hospital. They do tests on his vital functions. They can't find anything wrong. They put him on a drip. But his vital signs deteriorate. And then, just like that, he dies.

I have to admit I'm a bit of a sucker for this preposterous mumbo-jumbo. I can actually feel the hairs on the back of my neck stand up as I imagine myself in that engine room face-to-face with the unearthly. It was all his fault. My father had a gift for weaving story-spells. He'd suck you in—give you a ride on his flying carpet to exotic places that made you forget the cuts and bruises you experienced with him in real life.

When I was a kid, I was so caught up in the glamour of the stories that I didn't realise how racist they were. My dad always features in these tales as the Bwana. Black people figure in the stories as house-boys. Lovable characters with inferior flaws. They're smart but gullible. They're industrious but lazy. They're religious but pagan. They die of mumbo-jumbo.

My father doesn't mean to be racist but he is. Then it dawns on me that I've absorbed all these cartoon caricatures. All that time being fed stories about the black boys with their lazy smiles and their lazy ways. They seeped into my head and put their feet up. I got comfortable with them. I took it all for granted. I got stuck in the stories, my formative mind absorbing their inherent racism like it was taken for granted. My dad runs out of steam. He's slumped over the table almost asleep. So, I suggest we call it a night. I go to bed reeling from a combination of too much red wine and too much self-realisation.

The next day is a Saturday. The start of the weekend. The day of the installation of the new bath. The old bath was well past its prime. Its accretions and encrustations had taken the joy out of bathing. It had to go. I'd decided to install its replacement myself on account of the eye-watering bill, I'd had to pay when I got my builders to put a new shower in the upstairs bathroom. My dad had offered to help in the installation.

He got up as usual way before I surfaced. I went downstairs to find the healthy breakfast—muesli, yoghurt and grapefruit—I'd laid out the night before completely untouched. He was flitting busily over the stove, juggling pans, floating like a butterfly in that balletic boxers dance he'd never lost. I'm overpowered by the smell of singed flesh as he slaps a slab of bacon into my le Creuset skillet.

"Thought we could do with a good brekkie before we get started," he says, cracking eggs into a frying pan he's holding in one hand whilst jiggling the le

Creuset with the other. "I went to the corner shop. Got some nice Turkish sausage."

My head hurts too much to make a case for the resurrection of the Muesli. I sigh down at the table, resigned to a fry up. After a while, it's ceremoniously plonked down in front of me. A steaming Annapurna of bloated sausage, stratified bacon, shrieking black pudding, crepuscular fried bread and scorched eggs. He sets his own overflowing plate down next to mine, settles himself into the chair and begins to tuck in, forking down a mouthful of black pudding whilst leafing through the morning copy of the Daily Mirror.

I was apprehensive about the installation. My father had been accustomed over the years to fixing large things. Diesel engines the size of a house. Turning spanners as big as a rhinoceros to align the ship's tectonic plates.

My mother always said he didn't know when to stop. He always over-tightened things. He tried to build a greenhouse once but the delicacy of the operation maddened him. We'd sit indoors quaking as he laboured outside, the afternoon quiet punctuated by the sound of breaking glass. My mother said the smell of orchids made him dangerous.

The added concern is he's past his prime now —like the old bath. But I need to trust him. We need to work together. The problem is we've never agreed on anything. I remember coming back from my first year at University, my head expanded, soddened like a milk-soaked shredded wheat with Marx and Foucault. We had an argument in the cramped kitchen of his house.

My dad, the ex-trades union representative, turned Tory, forced to endure his son's fanatical socialist rant, paid for by his own generous contribution to the student grant. After about half an hour of my erratic maunderings on surplus value, he turns round to face me and says, "I'll tell you what. Why don't you sell the car I bought you and donate the proceeds to the fucking miners benevolent fund."

But we come to an accommodation for the bath installation. We work together. Start with the easy part—stripping out the old bath. In no time we've disconnected it, dragged it through the narrow doorway and down the stairs into the street, the father-son combo operating like a well-oiled diesel engine. It's when we begin to fill the void left by the old bath that the problems start. The big problem is navigating the new bath into the tight angle between two walls and then getting it to stay put.

It's like working with a giant tub of jelly. We get the edge of the bath lined up in the corner of the wall but it slips away again. We get the edge of the bath to stay put in the corner of the wall but the other end of the bath is listing like an overloaded trawler. We try to get the bath to horizontal by adjusting the height of its feet but this only serves to move it out of the corner.

We repeat this pattern forever—aligning the bath in the corner, adjusting the height of its feet, re-aligning the bath in the corner, re-adjusting the height of its feet. The air is blue with curses, matching the colour of the bruising I've accumulated on my thigh as I try to force the bath back where it belongs. Each of us is convinced, it's the other's fault this skittish thing isn't doing what it's told.

"Keep it in the corner," I yell, way too loud, as I adjust the bath's feet for the umpteenth time.

"It *is* in the fucking corner," he hisses back as the bath goes AWOL.

Then I see something dawning in his eyes.

"Battens," he shouts.

I take this as some sort of obscure maritime insult but before I can retaliate he's up on his feet and out of the bathroom. I hear him down in the cellar charging around like a demented squirrel then coming back up the stairs. He emerges framed in the bathroom door. He's clutching an armful of wood.

"Battens," he says, his voice amplified with triumph. "We need to screw the bath to the wall with battens."

And of course, he's dead right. Why didn't I think of it before. It's obvious. Just basic physics. Every action has an equal and opposite reaction. If you force a bath into a right angle that isn't exactly a right angle, it will have an effect on all the other angles. They all come out of line. We needed to nail that bastard bath to the wall with battens so it's stabilised and then we adjust its bastard feet so the whole thing is horizontal. Dad 1—Son 0. He's smirking like a halibut. He's put one over on his offspring. Just like the old days.

It's all plain sailing now. The bath—nailed to the wall like a penitent Catholic—is a subservient thing. It's as good as gold as we link its entrails to the household plumbing. My Father is humming a tune from what I believe to be HMS Pinafore as he connects the bath to the waste pipe. We're now in the final stage of the operation. His job is to do the last connections. My job is to go downstairs to check the water flow.

So, I wasn't upstairs when the catastrophe happened but in my mind, I see what happened. He fits a spanner in the nut below the mixer tap, turns and turns until it locks, puts all his weight into the spanner's shaft, turns and turns again and over-tightens and there's a crack and driblets of water form around the pipe, then merge together. I'm in the garden when the merged driblets swell into a flood that punctures the ceiling and rips downstairs. Cascades into the garden. Drowns the orchids.

June

Rehearsal Studio. Band Discussion. The Manager thinks we don't work well as a team. There's too many individual performances, she says and we don't come across as a tight unit. She announces a plan to enlist a psychologist to help improve the band's bonding. She hands out the proposed candidate's CV. We pass it around, each fingering it suspiciously as if it's a parking ticket.

"She's a fucking *sports* psychologist," exclaims Pete, waving the CV in disgust. "She works with *football* teams." He begins to recite the list of teams she's worked with. Barnet. Borehamwood. Bromley. Cheltenham Town. "It's not like it's the Premier League, is it?"

"They got to the semis of the Autoglass Trophy," says Flimsy, who's a keen student of the game.

"Who did?" asks Cyrus.

"Cheltenham," says Flimsy.

"How much does she cost?" asks Brendan.

The Manager quotes a fee of ten pounds an hour.

"When can she start?" asks Max.

Two days later, we assemble at the studio for our first meeting with Inga. She's blond, two metres tall and wears an Adidas tracksuit. There's a faint meniscus of sweat on her upper lip. She commands us to assemble in the middle of the studio—pronto—while she gives us a task. We respond with a consolidated wall of hostility. It's obviously already working, this team-bonding.

In this preliminary session, she explains, each of you will be blindfolded in turn. Then each one will fall backwards to the floor. This will help us to build the trust in each other. Everyone's confused. We're all looking at each other for a cue.

"What d'you mean," asks Pete, "by falling backwards to the floor?"

With a sigh redolent of having to explain very simple things to very small children Inga slowly and carefully maps out the task.

"You each get blindfolded," she says. "Then we decide on who goes in what order. The one who is doing the turn has to fall backwards. And the rest of you catch him. Or not," she sniggers.

"Fucking hell," mutters Pete as the insidiousness of the task dawns. "Might as well book my A&E appointment now."

No-one wants to go first. The Manager makes the necessary intervention. "The order of falling backwards will be decided by random selection." She takes one of the band's flyers and shreds it into sections. She writes a number on each section and then we each draw a number.

Flimsy goes first. She stands in the middle of the studio, arms flapping like a threatened pigeon.

"You better get close behind me," she shrills. "If I don't get caught, you're all fucking dead."

Panic sets in at the rear. We grab each other, forming a phalanx like in Ben-Hur.

"Are you ready," she shouts menacingly.

"Ready," shouts Pete.

Flimsy propels herself backwards. Though she lands in the middle of the phalanx the catchers are unprepared for the kinetic energy she'd put into the movement. We stagger for a moment like an ungainly crab before lowering her gently to the floor.

The thing is, it works. As we progress through the order, the band's confidence and trust increase. Pete pops backwards like a human cannonball, dropping unscathed into the safety net. Brendan does a reverse swan-dive.

"Six Points! Maximum score!" exclaims Inga, as she breaks into a round of applause.

The big test is Cyrus. You can sense the growing unease as he goes through his preparations.

"Are you ready," he bellows. 'Ready' is the ragged unconvincing response. He falls slowly, like a timbering Californian Redwood. Perfect landing. Dead centre. The phalanx absorbs the force, sagging slightly, then recovering. The Redwood has landed.

When it gets to my turn, I find myself looking forward to the abandonment of a lifetime of carefully cultivated inhibitions. I'm actually relishing the imminent sensation of relinquishing control to a bunch of muppets I wouldn't normally entrust with my shopping list. I steady myself at the moment, like a diver preparing for a thirty-metre plunge. Then slide backwards gracefully.

A microsecond later, I feel the sensation of my head smacking on the hard wooden floor of the studio. Through the mist of pain, I hear the rising crescendo of unsuppressed giggles.

When we've completed the bonding exercise, Inga takes her to leave. The band line up to bid her farewell, forming a guard of honour that wouldn't be out of place at a Wembley Cup Final. I'm last in line. I shake her hand as she heads past.

"Thanks, Inga," I say, "it was a life-changing experience."

She pierces me with the rapier look of someone who knows everything. "You didn't get catched," she says.

We take the collective learning from the bonding activity to next gig. World's End, Finsbury Park. Aptly named. The edge of civilised London. Come out of the Underground at Finsbury Park station, a giant transport octopus whose tentacles stretch in all directions.

Opposite is Rowans Tenpin—twenty-four-lane bowling alley, all neon and retro Americana. Turn left up Stroud Green Road in the direction of Crouch Hill, where Dave Stewart owned a studio called The Crypt and plotted the rise and rise of the Eurythmics. A couple of hundred metres and here we are. The World's End. Scotch egg. Sausage roll. Charter pie. Sunday roast. Table Football. Live Sports on the Big Screen. The Big Screen furled away when it's live music.

Soundcheck. Boxes ticked. Guitars tuned. Keyboard wheezing but passable. Drums as per usual. Sax is in tune. Singers sparring. Sprinkling of punters dotted round tables. No interest. No atmosphere. We're in for a long night. I take the opportunity to pilot test a song I'd written that adds to the stable of dark self-indulgent tear-jerkers that cluster around Come to My Rescue. It's called Shadow on My Soul.

I know what you're thinking. From the title, it looks like another self-indulgent first-stage-of-grief warble. And you'd be right. From start to finish, it rolls around in grief like a mongrel gyrating in a pile of shit in a municipal park. But it's refined grief. It's not your Tesco grief. It's more like your Marks and Spencer grief. There's some archly poetic lines. And musically it's top drawer grief. Here's what it feels like. It's 4/4, 85 BPM. I go straight into verse 1 without any intro. Cm7, followed by Fm7:

Shadow on my soul
Clouds smothering the warmth of the sun
Like a nightmare creeping in the shape of a dream
turning everything inside out
then the same repeated for verse 2:
The secrets we shared are public conversation
In times of love and war, there is no convention
Everything to lose and everything to gain
and the darkness falls.

Then the drums and guitars ramp the beat up for the first of a double chorus—
Fm, E♭, B♭:

There's no logic in love
no rational explanation
what is done is done
and can't be corrected
it's never the same.

Repeating the chords and beat for the second chorus:

There's no justice in love
No simple interpretation
When it's dead it's dead
and can't be resurrected
only a new beginning.

Verse 3 reverts back to the verse 1 formula:

Shadow on my soul
Moon drifting over sea of confusion
Broken promises and broken dreams
And the distance between us as wide as the ocean

And then the final verse, repeating the pattern, but with a twist in the last two
lines, moving from Fm7 to Fm, then E♭:

Shared understandings turn into accusations
souls stripped of compassion hearts hardened to feelings
Everyone's an island and everyone's to blame
and the curtain falls.

The thing is grief shifts CDs. Tell me Robbie Williams isn't a platinum-selling grief-wallower—think *Sexed Up*. Or George Michael—think *Jesus to a Child*. Number one in the UK charts and in six other European countries. Over half a million copies shifted in the US. Fair enough, coming home to find your partner's empty drawers—oo er Missus—and your Wurlitzer gone seems petty when set against the brutal demise of your heaven-sent love-for-life. But it's still grief.

People like songs about grief. Except for the people in the audience at The Worlds End. As I took Shadow on My Soul around the test circuit, I could sense the indifference building up. By the time I got to the middle eight, it had coagulated. I could almost see it hovering in front of the stage—a condensed ball of apathy that had a brownish-grey colour to it, like that slimy lump of sludge you extract from a blocked drain.

It didn't get any better as we cranked it up through the gears. We were still fighting the sludge. By the time we got to the final numbers, we were going through the motions. The performance ended with what I call a slattering of applause. Less than a smatter. But Inga's work had paid off.

As we packed up, the band showed off its newly acquired bonding skills.

"Shit gig," says Pete.

"Yeah, really shit," agrees Cyrus as he carefully slots the snare into its case like a pampered pet being bedded down for the night.

"Fucking shit," says Flimsy as she glides across the dance floor to the waiting Essex entourage.

"Shit audience—good job though—" says Brendan brightly, patting the remaining band members on the back as they stow their gear.

"Well done, guys," brays The Manager.

After the gig, The Manager and I head up the A41 to her boonie-house. She opens the front door. The usual scene of barely-restrained chaos reveals itself. As I enter I stumble over a child's scooter lurking in the shadows, one of its wheels amputated.

"Sorry," she giggles.

We bed down in her sanctuary—the only room in the house untouched by the carnage, its walls subtly attenuated by candles. She lights the incense burner. Luckily, we're too exhausted for sex. We slip into an entirely neutral slumber.

In the morning, there's a letter on the doormat. The Manager has received another response to the mail-shot. It's from an organisation called Red Eye. This is what it says:

Thank you for your CD which I received today.

At the moment, we are in the process of changing over from one main promoter to another so the promoters' office is not properly organised at the moment. I have just listened to your work and must say I was very impressed. Although I shall be extremely sorry to lose this CD, I shall pass it on to my colleague who will be taking over all of our promotions and bookings. I know she will contact you in the not-too-distant future.

Birth. Who needs it? I came reluctant into the world, six days later than advertised. Squeezed out like toothpaste dregs. Fingers prised from my mother's uterus dragged kicking and screaming into a hailstorm of choices. Sneak back into the womb and hope no-one would notice? Pretend to be stillborn? Make for the nearest breast? But which one—left or right?

I am often terrorised by a recurring birth dream where I'm encased in a small coracle, clinging to its side as I'm borne along at unfeasible speed by a vast tsunami of deep grey water, its surface writhing plumes of spray and foam. I burrow down in the dark below the waterline, helpless and powerless. This is the poetry of stuckness.

The big world I was born into was a paradox of convulsions and conservatism. There was the Korean War, nuclear tests, the Suez Crisis, the European Community, the Cuban Revolution, the Algerian Civil War, the Mau. A Conservative government was elected in Britain, promising to 'set the people free'. There was Brylcreem, Poodle skirts, Doris Day, Pat Boone, Lassie, the Lone Ranger, New Towns, the Festival of Britain, the Coronation of Elizabeth II and national service.

There was Benjamin Britten, Auden and Elliot; Joyce Grenfell and Noel Coward. There were carefully washed cars, clipped hedges, pressed trousers, patriotism, hanging, corporal punishment and homophobia. Gay men were referred to NHS specialists. Treatment included oestrogen to reduce libido;

psychoanalysis; religious counselling; electroconvulsive therapy; hypnosis; dating skills and encouragement to find a prostitute or female friend with whom to try sexual intercourse.

Though Liverpool was part of this broad canvas, it was on another planet entirely. Its inhabitants were a breed of voyagers and explorers, yet the city was fiercely insular and introspective. It cultivated independence and bloody-mindedness. The spirit of Merseyside was a spirit of contempt for officialdom and bureaucracy. It did things its way.

I was once in Rome going to the Colosseum, traversing the via del Fiori Imperiali. Along the route are three large-scale wall maps of the Roman Empire, depicting various stages in its growth. The bits of the map conquered by the Romans are coloured red. In 100 BC, the Empire is restricted to Italy, Greece, a small chunk of North Africa and half of Spain. By 54 BC, it has swallowed up all of Southern Europe, France, half of Britain, what is now Turkey and most of North Africa.

By 300 AD, the Roman Empire has added Egypt, a lot of the Middle East and all of Britain up to Hadrian's Wall. It may have been a trick of the light, but I swear that in the map that depicted the British Isles, there was a small oasis of yellow in the expanse of red. This oasis appeared to be Merseyside. It seemed obvious the armies of Claudius had reached the Mersey, took one look at the natives and headed for Chester instead.

I began to see signs of stuckness in the Scouse psyche; similar paradoxical survival strategies to those shown by the Reivers. The city was schizophrenic—riddled with contradictions. One contradiction was that Liverpool had always been an essentially conservative place, a product of mercantilism, colonialism and capitalism. It's wealth was built on the slave trade.

The iconic symbol of the city—the Liver Bird—is perched on top of buildings that were constructed on money acquired through the cotton plantation, the lash and the leg-iron. This mythical bird looks down on the street where slaves were chained, displayed and sold. Yet, though the merchants, ship-owners and traders made up the political elite and held the reins of power in the city, they presided over a large and vocal underclass whose persuasions were often in direct opposition to their own.

The underclass had a habit of baring its teeth. Over the last two centuries, Liverpool's history had been punctuated by radicalism, disobedience and public disorder. In 1819—well before the mass influx of Irish immigrants escaping the

Great Famine—Liverpool's first Orange march was chased off the streets by the Irish community.

Sixty years later, over 10,000 dockers and seamen went on strike for three weeks over pay reductions. This was a dress rehearsal for 1969 when the first national strike to affect a major car manufacturer, Ford, shut down the Halewood plant. Ten years later, widespread national labour disputes brought down the Labour government.

Liverpool's contribution, in typical laconic Scouse style, was a week-long grave-diggers strike. In the shipyards of Cammell Lairds, the dockyards of Bootle and the car factories of Halewood, bolshie shop stewards resisted time and motion studies and plotted the revolution. Then there was St Anthony's— The Anarchist-Communist Sunday School—which began meeting in November 1908—and whose members were seen on the streets in 1916 denouncing events like Empire Day, even though the school was notorious locally for its brutality.

The much more liberal-minded Scotland Road Free School, set up in the 1970s, was run on the principle of 'education in the community by the community'. There was no formal curriculum or timetable. Teachers 'guided' students towards an understanding of what 'freedom' meant.

The school was loathed by the local Catholic Mafiosi, who issued warnings of ex-communication should any parishioner dare to send their children to it. Finding it increasingly difficult to make ends meet, the school managers did a deal with Liverpool City Council, who guaranteed its funding.

In return, the school was obliged to take in students who had been barred from other schools in the area. The resultant mix proved too explosive and the school closed not long afterwards. True to form, the Catholic run schools in the area closed their own doors to former students of the Free School, on the grounds that they were 'ill-disciplined and backward'.

Scotland Road is the main thoroughfare's bounding the city's dock area. Though less than a mile long, it once had seventy-two pubs and distinguished itself by figuring prominently in some of the worst incidents of civil disobedience in Liverpool history. One of the most notorious was the Liverpool Police Strike of 1919, described by the Liverpool Daily Post as the 'worst outbreak of mob violence, looting and burning' Liverpool had ever seen.

The strike in Liverpool came a year after the successful national strike over police over pay and conditions. In Liverpool, two sections of the police had particular grievances: the mounted police and the traffic cops. Both sections worked a twelve hour shift but had to stay on duty for a full twenty-four hours when the shift structure changed. For these extra hours, they were paid peanuts.

One of the ironies of the Liverpool police strike was the attempt to link these grievances with broader workers' activism. Trade union leaders like Walter Citrine tried to persuade the Liverpool workers they should demonstrate in solidarity with the Police Union. But the fact was that organised labour hated the police. Liverpool workers and trade unionists had long memories of being battered by police truncheons during strikes and lock-outs in the docks.

The public in general were also no friends of the constabulary. Corruption and back-handers were rife in the force. Publicans were routinely expected to supply free ale to bobbies on the beat. Policemen took bribes to turn a blind eye to illegal bookmaking and in areas seen as crime-ridden the police maintained order by beating the shit out of the local population.

Cockified by their success the previous year, in August 1919 the National Union of Police and Prison Officers—NUPPO—demanded a pay increase, improved war bonuses, extension of their pension rights and the official recognition of NUPPO as the representative of the police workers. Unless their demands were met by midnight on the 29 August, they would call a strike. The next day, 12,000 men walked out. In Liverpool, half the City police force went on strike.

The consequences of the strike were far worse in Liverpool than anywhere else. On the Friday of the strike, the authorities had been able to concentrate their non-striking men in the most likely trouble spots and this consolidation of coppers was enough to maintain order. The following night was a different story. On Saturday morning, the Lord Mayor ordered all special constables to report for duty. He also made an appeal to Liverpool citizens to help the authorities preserve law and order.

Fat chance. The first shop to be looted was a jeweller. Gangs of youths then stripped the 'Mo-Go' chewing gum factory and other sweet factories. Their fathers targeted booze warehouses and off-licenses. One Liverpudlian who remembered the riots as a child said, "it was a chance to hit back for the hungry bellies, the bare feet, the squalor and four years of war."

In one of these raids, on a bottling plant, a looter—Cuthbert Howlett—was shot by one of the soldiers sent to prevent looting.

The Lord Mayor duly bottled it himself and got on the phone with the Home Secretary to say he couldn't guarantee public safety. The Home Secretary then asked the Duty Captain at the Admiralty to send in the Royal Navy. Though under-whelmed by the idea—the fleet was hundreds of miles away at Scapa Flow; most of the men had gone home for the August Bank Holiday and the military was not happy at helping out Scouse civilians—political pressure was applied.

The Admiralty then ordered the battleship Valiant to leave Scapa and sail to the Mersey, accompanied by the destroyers Venomous and Whitley. Rumours circulated that their commanders had orders to shell the city to keep the Scousers under control. In any case, the riots petered out after three days and a massive hangover. In the aftermath, more than three hundred Scousers were sentenced for their part in the bank Holiday weekend riot-fest.

The Police Strike of 1919 was further proof that it was there in our genes— the DNA of Reivers and Gallic warlords. We were stuck in the same old fucked up, paradoxical evolutionary survival strategies. The incipient rebelliousness; the street battles with the authorities; the opportunistic thieving. The two sides of the coin—insolently anarchic and deeply conformist. It was there in the stereotypes later constructed for us by Cockney comedians and Manchester United fans. Here's one, taken from a United supporters club website:

"Liverpool's newest big-name signing, a Bosnian international, has just scored on his debut for the club and immediately after the match phones his mum:

Bosnian-Scouser: Hello, Mum.

Mum: Hello, son, how was your debut?

B-S: Well, it went brilliantly. I scored in front of the Kop and we only lost 3-1.

Mum: That's wonderful. But I'm afraid that things here at home aren't so good.

B-S: Why, what's happened?

Mum: Well, this morning our car was set ablaze by a masked mob. They then broke into our house with baseball bats and battered your brother. They shot your father in the kneecaps, so he can't walk anymore and then raped your sister before moving on to the dog.

B-S: That's terrible—

Mum: I know. Why couldn't you have left us in Bosnia instead of bringing us to Liverpool?"

Wherever you looked, there was some joke about a scally Scouser, standing on a street corner, dressed in a shell-suit and waiting for a victim to turn up.

Why does the River Mersey run through Liverpool?

Because if it walked it would be mugged.

Man walks into a shop in Liverpool:

Man: Can I have a pair of tights for my wife?

Shop assistant: Certainly Sir, what size head is she?

What do you call a Scouser in a three-bed semi?

A burglar.

What do you call a Scouser in a suit?

The accused.

I went to see Terence Davies' magical documentary *Of Time and the City*, commissioned as part of Liverpool's 'European City of Culture' programme. There's a quote in Davies' voiceover from the nineteenth-century artist, Felice de Myrbach: 'If Liverpool did not exist it would have to be invented'.

The original quote was coined in a spirit of admiration when the city was an industrial and artistic powerhouse of the British Empire. Davies uses it in a Paradise Lost way. The film chronicles disintegration.

At the beginning of the film, quoting from A E Houseman, he describes the city as 'the land of lost content'. It's not hard to see why. The city was just as I remembered it through the hyper-vision of a child.

Rows of two-up-two-downs and scrubbed steps; sulphuric air mixed with the rich smell of hops from the breweries; cobblestones, bomb craters and demolition sites; hair-nets and cloth caps. There was the overhead railway, with its intricate lattice-work of iron bridges and walkways. My grandfather, a socialist and Fenian, used to walk me over it, my hand in his and indoctrinate me with tales of the revolution and the men behind the wire.

My other grandfather, the one on the Kinmont Willie side, used to run a shop near Upper Parliament Street, in the heart of Toxteth—Liverpool 8, as we knew it. Or more accurately, my grandmother ran it. My grandmother scared me. She was a formidable woman. She wasn't large in stature, but she had a manner that could reduce all the street hard men to forelock-tuggers.

In her presence, the enormous Alsatian that guarded the back entrance to the shop, which would launch itself in a whirlwind of teeth and fur in the direction of any human who ventured across its line of sight, would whimper and grovel.

Over the rims of her outsize spectacles, she would give you a look that managed to effortlessly combine both pity and distaste.

She was absolute monarch of the big edifice in Warwick Street that housed both the family living quarters and its economic mode of production. From the ground floor shop, she dispensed cigarettes, newspapers, tinned spam, Mars bars and firelighters to the diverse and exotic diaspora that constituted the Toxteth community, with its dockers and sailors, factory workers, thieves and vagabonds, its Irish, Chinese and Jamaicans.

No matter what meteorological mix was served up on any given day—rasping heat or searing cold—she kept a cavernous Aga continuously blazing. Roast lamb was permanently on tap and the kitchen was open to anyone passing who needed to be fed.

Toxteth was a small but perfectly formed Palaeozoic lagoon with its own rich primal soup. Here, an exotic convocation of replicators assembled themselves and jostled for supremacy. One of them emerged to dominate the rest—scouserous scallious. It was equipped with a formidable array of tools to flourish in its inhospitable environment.

There were the extended arms, unfeasibly long and lithe, like those of a slender Loris, perfectly adapted to poke through the bars of security grilles. There were the short, muscular lower limbs that could propel their survival machine through the Toxteth streets at a speed easily capable of out-running the fleetest shop-owner or police constable.

Through negative feedback and extended phenotyping, scouserous scallious had acquired an equally formidable set of purposive behaviours that complemented these tools. It could blend into the background, adopting through camouflage the grainy hues and textures of its habitat. In extremis, it became completely invisible, integrating so seamlessly with its surroundings that, when questioned in the event of a break-in or mugging, it could claim that it simply wasn't there.

Then there was the group alarm. Like meerkats, scouserous scallious had developed a system of look-outs and bell-ringers. When triggered, in situations where discovery or apprehension was imminent, the air would oscillate an orchestrated, high-pitched nasal twang that warned of the impending peril.

The shop my grandparents owned was one of the places where scouserous scallius tested out and honed these survival strategies. Although, because of the open house feeding policy, a basic honour code protected it to some extent from predators, there were still enough scallies around to make it a target.

We woke up one day to find the Alsatian dog lifeless in a pool of blood and brains, battered to death with the handle of a washing-press. The shop had been ransacked, the intruders long gone. But my grandmother, too, evolved. She developed her own tools and strategies. The unfeasibly huge forearm, with the girth of a sumo wrestler, precision engineered to wield the police truncheon kept behind the counter. The spare set of eyes fixed firmly on the back of the head.

Life in the shop was an endless joust between competing replicators. Thieving was a common strand across gene pools. Everyone was at it. Even members of my own extended family. My father told me a story of when he lived above the shop. He was constantly pilfering the cigarettes that were kept in a cupboard at floor level, as well as any spare cash he could get his hands on.

Though formidable, my grandmother, in his words, was also a bit of a drama queen. Her forte, in times of severe stress, was to go into a fainting swoon. On one occasion when this happened, my father took advantage of the opportunity to relieve her purse of several notes, which he added to the pile of cash exchanged for thieved cigarettes and alcohol.

And then there was the arson. In 1981, Liverpool's citizens once again took to the streets. This time it happened where I grew up, in Toxteth. Once more, it was police versus scallies. The spark that ignited nine days of setting buildings on fire, street battles with police and looting of stores was the arrest of Leroy Cooper.

As with the 1919 riot, relations between police and civilians were not at their best. The Merseyside force had a particularly bad reputation in the area for stopping and searching black youths under the hated 'sus' laws. Officers were frequently accused of 'farming'—planting drugs on youths. There was a perception in the community of heavy-handed policing, harassment and arrests for trivial reasons, like hanging around on your own street corner. In this atmosphere, the police made a big mistake. They arrested Leroy in front of a large crowd of locals.

In another parallel with the 1919 riot, the ferocity of the resultant mayhem was completely underestimated by the authorities. Rioters attacked supermarkets, firebombed a bank and numerous other businesses and burnt down a sports club on Upper Parliament Street.

The riot spread to other neighbourhoods that were predominantly white working class. Losing control of the situation, the police fired CS gas canisters—the first time CS had been used in mainland Britain, outside Northern Ireland. Police reinforcements were called in from as far away as Cumbria, the West Midlands and Devon in a desperate effort to control the burning streets.

In another parallel with the 1919 riot, one rioter was killed—this time not shot but run over by a police Land Rover. After the first week of rioting, Merseyside Police Chief Constable Kenneth Oxford said that 468 police officers had been injured, 500 people arrested and at least 70 buildings demolished, though other estimates suggested up to 1,000 police were injured and double the number of buildings destroyed.

The Chief Constable called the riot 'the work of thieves and vagabonds who needed no excuse for violence and destruction'. Yet, the Chair of the Merseyside Police Committee, Margaret Simey, more accurately fingered the underlying conditions-the bad housing; the unemployment; the police harassment—that had led to the riot.

She said of the rioters, "They would be apathetic fools—if they didn't protest."

July

Flimsy is late for band rehearsal. She'd gone down to Soho. Interview in Greek Street for a Government radio ad. They're targeting TV license-dodgers. She was expecting a posh gaff but the office is a couple of rooms above a Chinese take-away. Up some rickety stairs to reception with some old girl polishing her trotters. Points her to a sofa that's seen better days. The magazines are all out of date. Tatty really. She waits.

Eventually, a bloke turns up. He's wearing a tartan kilt and headphones. Let me escort you to the studio he says. They walk down a narrow corridor. It's a bit close. Uncomfortable. The studio is a tip. Empty fag packets and full ashtrays. Cables snaking all over the place. Gaffer tape everywhere. There's a sound booth in the corner enclosed in glass. It's smaller than your average toilet. Tartan Kilt asks for a microphone test. Flimsy riffs a couple of lines from Porgy and Bess. The bloke seems satisfied.

He hands her the script. It's always a shocker when you first see an advert jingle. She's never prepared. She's done jingles for breakfast cereals. Snap crackle and pop. The worst was an advert for car silencers. Some genius from the ad agency thought it would be a good idea to do the ad with no vocal sound. She stood at the microphone for ten minutes just breathing. Did ten takes. But at least she got paid.

This one's a thirty second ad. It's a variation on 'Are you sitting comfortably'. It begins by setting the scene. You're sitting watching your favourite TV show unaware that outside in the street the TV Detector Van is closing in. Then she does the anxiety-raising bit. The sophisticated technology inside the TV Detector Van picks up the electromagnetic radiation from your TV. The Van is heading straight towards you. There is no escape. Then she does the punishment bit. You could be fined up to a thousand pounds if you get caught watching TV without a licence.

Finally, there's the avoid the shame bit. Get your licence today. You can pay in easily affordable monthly instalments. It's all bollocks, of course. The detector vans don't have any electromagnetic radiation detection equipment. And even if they did, there's only about five of them to cover the entire country.

Despite the bollocks, the advert needs to be persuasive. Tartan Kilt thinks she sounds too timid on the punishment bit. He says she needs to put more emphasis on the 'you could be fined up to a thousand pounds if you are caught watching TV without a licence' line. Give it more volume. Give it more dominatrix.

They do three more takes before he's happy with it. Then she has to do more work on the 'avoid the shame' bit. It's the opposite of the punishment bit. He says she needs to sound more tough love—like she's the best pal of the tight bastard who dodges their TV licence but at the same time she gently persuades them to pay up. They do another six takes before he's satisfied she's got the right balance between mate and magistrate.

She thinks it's not a million years away from the stuff she does in the band. She thinks she doesn't have any say in what she performs. The lead singer gives her the song sheet. It tells her what to sing and when to sing it. It's got nothing to do with what she feels. It may as well be a radio jingle.

This band—it's just a stepping stone really. They call her the backing singer but she's too good for that. She knows she's got a much better voice than that pretentious dick of a lead singer. Everyone says so. Max. Cyrus. Even Brendan and Duff. Her dad thinks they should give her the lead on some of the songs. Like Come to My Rescue and Dirty Linen. She thinks she should lead on all of them.

I'm going through the set list for tomorrow's gig when Flimsy arrives. She makes a half-hearted apology for the lateness. Seems she's been doing a radio jingle.

"Well done, Flims," gushes Max. "What was it for?"

Flimsy looks a tad embarrassed. "It's for the Government," she says. "TV License dodgers."

Max looks a bit shifty and turns to attend to his sax. I get back to the set list. The gig's at The Feathers. Ealing Broadway. On the surface another bangers and mash job. But The Feathers has history.

In April 1967, Pink Floyd played its 'Blue Opera Club' night. By all accounts, it didn't go down well. In an interview with Zig Zag magazine, reprised in Julian Palacios' book *Syd Barrett and Pink Floyd: Dark Globe*, Roger Waters recalls the moment when a member of the audience threw 'a heavy copper penny coin' at his head.

"The worst thing that ever happened to me was at the Feathers Club," said Waters. He described, "A bloody great cut in the middle of my forehead. I bled quite a lot. I stood right at the front of the stage to see if I could see him throw one. I was glowering in a real rage. I was going to leap into the audience and get him. Happily, one freak turned up who liked us, so the audience spent the whole evening beating the shit out of him and left us alone."

It was one of Pink Floyd's last gigs before their first overseas performance of 'Arnold Lane' on the 'Fan Club' pop music TV show in Zaandam in the Netherlands. After their stint on the show, they caught the last flight out of Amsterdam to appear at 3 AM at the 14 hour Technicolour Dream Concert at Alexandra Palace in London with thirty other bands including Soft Machine, The Move and The Pretty Things, turning up according to some reports completely off their faces.

I'm thinking we need a song like Interstellar Overdrive in our set-list to generate audience antipathy. Antipathy generates energy. Energy generates excess. Excess generates headlines. But we don't have anything in our locker that resembles the kind of ponderous psychedelic space rock that incited a yob in the crowd to try to decapitate Roger Waters with a penny. The closest number we have is Words and Intentions.

Musically, with its distinctly reggae feel, it doesn't remotely resemble anything in the Pink Floyd repertoire, but I reckon its political posturing—a strident critique of the way our country still clings to its colonialist delusions—is bound to wind up your average yob. I look forward to introducing it.

We make our way through the set list, using the Big Dipper model. After the routine Cantaloupe opener, we do the usual two ballads to soften the audience up, starting off with Dirty Linen, followed by Hunger. To be honest, Hunger is a cringey amalgamation of Mills and Boon pulp romance and pop psychology. It's like I took a pattern from Cliche Monthly and knitted a song that pushes all the buttons: bed-sit angst, Laura Ashley prints, mid-morning therapy sessions and the very worst of Stock-Aitken-Waterman.

At 80 BPM, it's a slow-moving tune—the uncharitable might call it pedestrian—with a Latin-jazz feel to it. Because there's a lack of invention in the musical structure—it's basically a four-chord shit-kicker—I felt it needed to generate some interest so I inverted the usual formula and started with the chorus. There's a four bar acoustic guitar intro running into the opening chorus, which goes D, C, D, C, slipping from C to B♭ in the last line:

I get stronger
thinking about your love
and I hunger
to do all the things I'm thinking of
and the longer
I'm staying inside your world
I can really be
I can really feel the soul in me.

The guitar intro repeats leading into the first verse—D, B♭, D, B♭, then B♭, C, D, B♭.

When I was a child all the while I was kept inside myself
Don't want don't feel don't touch
don't give anything away
I was empty as the desert sand
then you were there to change it into Summerland.

We repeat the chorus straight, then there's the obligatory middle eight bars of instrumental, on tenor sax, before a repetition of verse 1. The acoustic guitar instrumental pays another visit before we end with a reprise of the chorus.

We needn't have bothered with the ballads. How can you soften up an audience that's already comatose. When we get to Words and Intentions I'm scanning the room, longing for the heavy copper coin that floored Roger Waters to scythe its way towards my head. It never comes. All I see is an audience atrophied in beer and torpor. There's two young blokes doing a half-hearted pogo at the front of the stage as the throbbing bass line kicks in, but the reality is we're competing for attention with a darts match in the corner of the bar. The Feathers turn out to be exactly what it says on the tin. Bangers and Mash.

Two days later, we re-group for a rehearsal. The Manager brings tidings. There's a letter from BBC Radio. This is what it says:

Thanks for sending me your CD.

I really liked the first track and, consequently, took it to our weekly playlist meeting, where it was received reasonably well. Most producers liked the guitar and overall feel of the song but thought it would benefit from a greater level of production (I know this is impossible where funds are limited). We also felt that the vocals could be stronger.

If you haven't already done so then I would suggest you send a copy to Johnny Walker.

Good luck. Keep believing and persevering and you're halfway there.

The Manager sends the CD to Johnny Walker. A few days later there's another letter. This time from BBC Radio 1 FM. It says:

Sorry, this is not for me. Have you tried Andy Kershaw or John Peel?

The Manager sends the CD to Andy Kershaw and John Peel.

Arson was in my genes. When I was fourteen, I started a guerrilla campaign against stuckness. It began with a modest act of pyromania. There was an Elder tree at the far end of the school playing field, close to the railings that separated the main building from the motorway.

Legend has it, in Celtic folklore, that the Elder—the Queen of Trees; the wise woman spirit; the Hylde-moðer—is used in exorcism to summon gods like Dagda and Nuada. It's used in healing rituals. You can make magic wands from its branches to ward off evil attacks. If you're so minded, you can wear its twigs as amulets. And if planted in open land it can save you from a lightning strike.

For me, the Elder's properties were more prosaic. Its trunk and leaves provided excellent smoking cover. At peak times, during break and lunch, only the faintest outline of the Hylde-moðer could be distinguished beneath a Vesuvian fug ignited by scores of Park Drives and Embassy Regals. I spent more hours than I care to remember pressed close to the Tree-Queen's ample, indurate skirts. Smoking.

I became intimate with her topography. Running the hand that wasn't clamped to a cigarette over her rough integument, I catalogued every woody crenelation; every laugh-line and crow's foot that endowed her with a regal, alluring maturity. I memorised each hormonal catastrophe that had been carved in her forgiving flesh, with its atlas of adolescent longings and desires.

It seems barely credible that I should choose this mother-spirit to be the subject of my first steps on the road to rebellion. But I don't blame myself. I blame extended phenotyping. I wanted to destroy the tree in the same spirit my ancestors used to destroy their own habitat. When I struck the spark that lit the paraffin I'd applied to the trunk of my tree of desire I was simply doing what my survival machine was programmed to do.

If I had been expecting some instant catharsis from this act of matricide; some muscular convulsion of the soul, I was to be disappointed. It was a dank Lancashire night, the air obese with imminent rain. The first flame tongued thrillingly from the tree but then shrank back as if cowed by its complicity. It rallied momentarily, then died.

I re-loaded the Zippo; took aim and fired. Same result. Hylde-moðer wasn't about to go gracefully. I unscrewed the paraffin container and gave her another dousing. I applied ignition. Nothing happened. Hylde-moðer 1, extended phenotyping nil. I indulged myself in a random act of compensatory gratification by torching the surrounding turf, then trudged homeward.

Half an hour later, my birth mother opened up in response to the unexpected call of the door chime to be met by a vision of her diminutive progeny flanked by two towering pillars of the Merseyside constabulary, one of whom was holding up a paraffin-can, its rust-flaked outline mutely accusing. They accepted the invitation to come inside and the offer of tea and Eccles cakes, with the faint scepticism of ones accustomed to acts of bribery. What followed is a textbook example of what ethnomethodologists call the social construction of meaning.

Birth Mother: "What's he done?"

PC1: "We found him climbing over the school gates carrying this paraffin container."

Birth Mother: "So?"

PC2: "We saw some smoke coming from the school grounds. When we went in, we found some smouldering grass and some scorch marks on a tree."

Birth Mother: "What does he say about it?"

PC2: "Your son claims he was re-enacting the biblical episode of the burning bush in order to gain a more grounded experience for his religious studies exam."

Birth Mother: "Exactly."

PC1: "It's a serious matter, madam. The police take a dim view of people wandering around at night carrying flammable materials and setting fire to things."

Birth Mother: "He's only fourteen. Youse should be out catching criminals not persecuting young lads who want to better themselves."

I had carried the arson gene with me, from the docks to the new town. In a more modest re-run of the epic migrations my clans had made in the previous centuries, we moved across an increasingly atomised cityscape. It was just as Terence Davies painted it in his documentary.

Time had rendered the city. People were uprooted to prefabricated suburbs like Roughwood—with its high rises and piss-stained elevators; its' graffiti proclaiming 'this is a no go area—enter at own risk'. We were relocated from the Liverpool docks to Westvale, a suburb of the Kirkby new town, next to Roughwood, when I was about six years old. There, I watched evolution further unfold.

Where I lived, a particular sub-group had refined Meerkat behaviour into an art form. It was called the Dummy Gang. Built on a complex network of extended siblings, the Dummy Gang specialised in supermarket raids. It was composed entirely of children and juveniles, assembled in age and size range like a Babushka doll. It had developed an elegant, beautifully equipped strategy for supermarket raiding.

In these, the relatively early days of retail security systems, many shops had infrared sensors. Not all of these were optimally positioned. In some cases, there would be around a foot or two of the immediate ground floor area not covered by the sensors. The Gang would identify suitable targets and gather around outside. The middle-sized and mid-aged would be posted as look-outs.

Once the entrance door had been jemmied, the youngest and smallest would crawl along the floor, under the sensor and snatch easily portable, high-value goods. These would be passed down the line to the door, where they would be seized and spirited away by the older and bigger gang members. Watching the Dummy Gang at work was a spectator sport for many kids in the neighbourhood. In a place where disposable income was negligible and TV sets scarce it was the only show in town.

The new environment threw up adaptive challenges. We responded with creativity and ingenuity. Kirkby new town was one of the biggest of its kind in Europe. There were more under 16's than anywhere else on the Continent. Yet, there were virtually no services. The place was an enormous building site, oases of housing surrounded by vast acres of corrugated earth, churned up by bulldozers. In the absence of playgrounds, we rolled around in lime pits. No swimming pool? No problem. We splashed in muddy craters left by pile drivers. In this new soup, the Reiver genes flourished.

My older sisters were hanging out with a crowd of jack the lads from the estate. They were sound boys—but partial to a spot of opportunistic thieving. Opportunity knocked in the shape of entrepreneurism, which filled the large holes in Kirkby's service infrastructure.

Into one such hole regularly chugged an old single-decker converted bus—known locally as 'the Mobile'. Its windows had been replaced with welded steel plates. Where seats used to be were shelves stretching the length of its narrow interior, all piled high with perishable goods. Left parked overnight, it was a sitting target.

One such night, my sisters' suitors abetted by a posse of their mates, decided to go on a bus raid. The plan was simple. They would enter the padlocked rear door using bolt cutters. Then, because the bus gangway wasn't wide enough for more than one person, they would form an Indian file, one behind the other and pass out the goods to the last man standing outside the bus, who would place the contraband in a swag-bag.

The plan was working perfectly. Half the Mobile's contents had been spirited away. The last man in the line was congratulating himself on a smooth bit of team-work when he felt a nudge at the rear, disconcertingly targeted at the precise centre where his upraised buttocks protruded into the night air. He wafted a backhander in the direction of the swag-man, convinced he was being subjected to an old juvenile jape. He felt another nudge, this time more urgent and more penetrating.

"Fuck off and stop messing about," he shouted, turning round to confront his aggressor. A large police dog met his gaze, attached to an even larger policeman. Beyond him, the swagman could make out the dim shapes of other policemen, their toothy smiles punctuating the surrounding gloom.

You could think of Kirkby new town as a kind of bad gene sink—the outcome of the repatriation of thousands of Scouse families from areas around Liverpool that was notoriously mean or bolshie or crime-ridden. Kirkby was an experiment in social engineering.

It re-housed many of the city's poor and problem families in tower blocks that bore little resemblance to Courbusier's 'Unite d'habitation'. It's possible that this spatial and social concentration of anomie and dysfunctionality had a hot-housing effect. What is certainly true is that the new town gained a dark reputation. Here's how one commuter describes his daily train trip to Liverpool via Kirkby:

"The chavs that populate the bridge above the station are the trolls from fairy tales, only on top of the bridge instead of beneath. Newton discovered gravity in 1687. In 2004, the shit of the earth, more commonly known to us as 'chavs' that populate Kirkby have decided to test his theory using bricks.

"I'm glad that in my wait for the next train, I have to endure something akin to a day in the life of a resident in Baghdad—it's nice to know these little shits will gladly come out even in the rain just to continue this bombardment of the 'evil' people that wait patiently for the train either to or from work, just so we can pay for these little shits to afford the beer (for beer read piss!) they drink on a daily basis instead of doing the decent thing and getting a job!"

It's all there again. The usual stereotypes—anti-social; violent; work-shy. In 1993, Kirkby hit the world headlines when the body of a two-year-old kid from the new town was found on a railway line. It had been neatly severed by a passing train.

However, a forensic pathologist who examined the child's body concluded that he had already been dead before the train cut his body in two. The boy, James Bulger, had suffered so many injuries, including a fractured skull, that it was impossible to attribute a particular blow as the fatal one. Two ten-year-old boys, Jon Venables and Robert Thompson, both from the nearby district of Walton, were arrested, charged and later convicted for Jamie Bulger's murder.

August

London enjoys a short sweltering period when the thermometer soars above the low twenties. The Manager takes advantage of the good weather to organise another session with Inga. Inga turns up at the rehearsal studio wearing a padded parka and climbing boots. She's carrying a Sports Direct holdall. This time the band is more welcoming, greeting her like a potentate sent by an oil Sheik.

In this workshop, she says in the clipped tones of a GCSE invigilator we will improve audience relations. We will use the role-play tools to explore how it feels from the point of view of a punter hearing your works. We will learn how to make an audience love us and learn how to subjugate an audience who doesn't love us.

Without warning, she turns directly to me. Hello Fuckface says Inga. Taken aback I have no time to camouflage my response. I'm already rearing up at her fists automatically clenched in that aggressive posture I'd adopt if someone out of the blue called me Fuckface on a Dalston street. You see, Inga says, turning to address the band. Already we have the classic response of an individual lacking the correct skills to manage a negative social interaction. The band are nodding their heads. I feel like a complete muppet.

Inga moves to the centre of the studio. Steadies herself. Adopts a commanding posture. Imagine this is Wembley Stadium she says sweeping her arm theatrically to encompass the studio's cramped confines. I try to extrapolate the band from here to Wembley Stadium. It somehow doesn't come out right. Inga gives out a chuckle.

"Don't worry about it," she says. "It doesn't matter if it's this small space or Wembley Stadium. The rules of audience interaction are the same."

She picks up the holdall. Unzips it. Pulls out a collapsible flip chart stand that she efficiently un-collapses. Pulls a flip chart pad out of the holdall and secures it to the stand. Positions herself in front of the stand, brandishing a felt top marker pen.

"These are the rules of audience interaction," she says. "There are five rules." She scribbles each rule on the flip chart.

Rule 1: Never look the audience in the eye. Fix your gaze on a point above the audience. From their perspective, it looks like you are looking at them. From your perspective, all you can see is the ceiling. This means you will not be distracted.

Rule 2: Never let the audience become the boss. You must cow the audience from the start. Make sure they know they are subservient creatures. Their role is to consume and amplify your genius. And to buy merchandise at the end of the gig, if it is offered.

Rule 3: Always have a strategic response to a bad audience reaction. You must never take personally any negative response, such as booing or catcalling. Bear in mind these responses reflect the stupidity of the audience. You must respond with positive feelings to get the audience on your side.

Rule 4: Seduce the audience into thinking every song you play is a personal message to each individual member of the audience. Your ultimate aim is thousands of socially retarded individuals masturbating in front of your poster in the bedrooms of their low-life low-rise apartments.

Rule 5: Always leave the audience with the illusion they are taking away something from the encounter that is personal to them. This means that at the end of your performance, you must introduce all of your selves to the audience personally so they can add this to their masturbation activities in their low-life low-rise apartments.

Following her presentation, Inga takes us through some exercises designed to improve our audience relations. We practice peering at the ceiling. Duff complains he can't see the keyboard. We frolic in audience encounter role play. Pete takes on the role of the aggressive drunk. Butting up to me in that stabbing street-pigeon stance. Spitting insults right in my face. Loving it. I take on Yogic mindfulness. Absorb the insults. Let them go. Revenge is a dish best served on the cool stage of the Monterey Jazz Festival.

At the end of the audience relations session, Inga takes her leave. The band line up to bid her farewell, forming a guard of honour. I'm last in line. I shake her hand as she heads past.

"Thanks, Inga," I say, "It was a life-changing experience."

She pierces me with that rapier look. "Auf Weidersehen Fuckface," she says.

Out to North London for a gig at the Blue Man in Kingsbury. It's one of those suburban backwaters you end up in if you can't afford the rent in decrepit but cool areas like Shoreditch or Dalston. You can get to it accidentally if you're heading for Brent Cross shopping centre, miss the turning on the M1 and panic. The Blue Man is one of those mock-baronial style pubs with large chimney-stacks, a biergarten and ivy clogging the walls. It serves pie and chips at lunchtime and has a children's playground in the garden.

We arrive for the sound check early evening. It's not looking promising. Already the pub is filling up with a crowd of testosterone-fuelled youth necking pints as if a new prohibition law is imminent. An argument breaks out at the snooker table over a miss-potted black. Snooker cues are raised threateningly. One of the bar staff breaks it up. But you can see the embers still smouldering.

We assemble on stage. I start the introductions, following Inga Rule 4.

"Hello, Kingsbury. How you doin' tonight? It's great to be here. We're gonna take you through the evening with a great set of songs we hope each and every one of you will love. To start off, here's the band to give a personal hello to you all. I'll be back soon. Hold tight."

The band crank up with Cantaloupe. As they smooth through the gears I already detect rumblings of discontent from the youth posse. One of them turns to his mate. "Oi Frankie," he shouts, "that bird on the stage—is that yer mum?"

I'm sending out thought waves to Flimsy. Rule 3. Rule 3. Give the twat a smile. Gather him into your warm embrace. Characteristically perverse, Flimsy responds with Rule 2, skewering the youth with a scowl that almost pins him to the floor.

I'm starting to think Inga's audience relations methodology might not be seamlessly transferable from Doc Marten football grounds to pub music venues. In this business, you have three types of audience.

The first type is passive. Either they're your fan club and they love you anyway or they don't know you but you're playing in a genteel venue where the audience is well-behaved. The second type is active. They don't know you and they will either love you at the end of the set or fuck off home in indifference. The third type is the worst. They're hyperactive. They give you a hard time throughout and if you're lucky they'll fuck off home without doing you damage.

The Blue Man audience is the third type. From the off, we're not struggling to get their attention. We're struggling to avoid their attention. It's the youth posse. They have no interest in ballads. Dirty Linen goes down like a sudden influx of herpes. Neither, it turns out, do they have any interest in political discourse. Like Heart of England, the inspiration for Words and Intentions came from stories I'd picked up from Max and Cyrus about what it was like to be part of a family that was prominent in government in a fragile regime in Africa.

The contradiction of living in a country ranked one of the highest in the world in natural resources and ranked one of the poorest on GDP. The pervading stench of corruption. The chasm between what was promised to people and what was delivered. The pervasive fear of that early morning knock on the door, opening it to be confronted by an army colonel. Both their families had been forced to flee after that knock on the door. Both were living in exile after the inevitable coup.

I followed 'Dirty Linen' with Words and Intentions hoping the change in tone from balladeering to tub-thumping would rouse the rabble. It starts with four bars of clangy, scratchy rhythm guitar leading into the first verse, Dm7, G7:

Government say there'll be food tomorrow
People say we need food today
Government say there'll be bread tomorrow
People say we need bread today

then the keyboard surfs you upwards on an ascending scale F7, C7, Dm7, G7

Nothing's what it seems
Man come sell you dreams
Signing there on the line
Land of plenty future fine

before repeating the sequence

Knocking on your door
Promising the earth and more
Give me your tired and your poor
Believe it will be better than it was before

then reverting to the first verse structure

And the government say there'll be work tomorrow
And the people say we need work today
And the government say there'll be work tomorrow
But the people say we need work today.

Before closing in on the killer line:
How can we survive on words and intentions (X2).

There's an eight-bar steel pan instrumental that leads into another eight bars with the whole band chanting.

How can we survive on words and intentions before the instruments kick back in and the killer line repeats over sixteen bars of vocal-instrumental improvisation before coming to a sudden crescendo stop.

'Words and Intentions' is met with a collective sigh of boredom. I go for 'Ordinary Madness' to bring them into line. The song pulls them back in momentarily. Its frantic up-tempo gets them up on their feet. It's when we get to 'Come to my Rescue' that the real trouble starts.

The trick to 'Come to My Rescue' is that you fill the song with space. The space allows time for the song to breathe. The breath in the song creates tension. If you're actually listening to and getting involved in the song as opposed to letting the song become part of the background white noise you allow the first verse to take you into an empty room.

You feel the emptiness of the room. The minimalist instrumental accompaniment to the vocals adds to the emptiness. The second verse expands on the emptiness. You're taken from the room to an empty house and then on to an empty life. The emptiness zooms out exponentially and you feel you're in an empty universe. Then the song cranks up and the female counterpoint of the duet kicks in, releasing the tension but creating a different—sexual—tension.

I might as well have packed the set list with Joe Jackson covers. It's obvious the craft of Come to My Rescue is wasted on the Blue Man. Halfway through verse one I can already see they've lost interest. Become restless. They're necking pints. Mock-fighting each other. Murmuring discontent. "Get off, Grandad," I hear through the rumble. I soldier on.

But when Flimsy comes in on the counterpoint, the whole thing kicks off. From the audience, the same voice that disturbed the set intro cuts through, "Oi Frankie. Yer mum's back on."

Flimsy clocks it. She glowers then presses on. She's climbing into third gear in the second counterpoint when one of the youth posse struts in front of the stage. He leans backwards thrusting his groin forwards. "Oi MILF," he shouts. "Rescue this."

Flimsy's response is beautifully calibrated. Instead of jumping off the stage to retaliate, she maintains a position of band superiority—Rule 2—then launches a perfectly placed gobbet of phlegm directly into his face. He goes ballistic. Jumps forward onto the stage. Pete aims a boot that sends him back into the audience. His mates rush forward to join the assault. What they haven't factored into the equation is that in the interval between sound check and performance Flimsy's entourage has arrived on the dance floor.

Suddenly, the melee at the front of the stage is swelled by Flimsy's dad, several uncles and a significant proportion of the Essex Mafia. From my position on stage, I see Flimsy's dad floor one of the posse with a savage uppercut. I adopt Rule 1 to blank out audience distraction, fixing my gaze on the ceiling above the bar. I didn't see it coming. Luckily, the bottle didn't hit me full-on. It glances off my temple. I'm almost poleaxed, staggering with the shock, before recovering. Then there's a hail of bottles.

It takes twenty minutes or so before peace breaks out, accelerated by the arrival of the Metropolitan Police. We never got to Rule 5. The gig was officially abandoned after 'Come to My Rescue'. We had to endure an unedifying wrangle over whether our full fee would be paid due to its premature end and the damage incurred as a result of what the officers described as a mini-riot. The Manager agrees a dignified settlement.

After the gig, I need an antidote to the mayhem. Down to the Mangal Ocakbasi for a very late supper. Ali theatrically ushers me to a table. En route, I pass Gilbert and George—the Living Sculptures—almost identically matched in tweed suits and patterned ties, perched opposite each other at their permanently reserved summer table, although it's only just turning Spring. In winter, they're moved closer to the grill so they can heat up. The grill's fiery temperature has the added benefit of discouraging tourists who turn up to watch them eat.

I've been passing Gilbert and George's table off and on for over a decade now, without the slightest nod of recognition. Ali guides me to a table just behind

124

them. As I watch tourists watching them, I'm minded of arthropods fired in amber. I vacillate over the menu between pirzola and pan-fried liver, envying the impeccable precision of Gilbert and George.

The pirzola wins out, but it's hard to enjoy it. The Mangal has filled up. Rammed to the rafters, its narrow architecture, sparse wooden floor and thin uninsulated walls make for unforgiving acoustics. Each braying outburst from the Timberland and Plaid Shirt wearers packing the groaning tables amplifies and combines to become a wall of shrieks. I finish quickly, pay up and head to the Red Art, passing Gilbert and George on my way out. They fail to nod in my direction.

The Red Art has become my creative lodestone. I go there on song-writing missions, deluding myself that the ridiculously strong espresso and cheap Tempranillo it dispenses will get the juices flowing.

The Red Art is so called because it's painted red and it sells art. Works by local daubers hang on every available wall space, illuminated from above by ceiling lamps which have the appearance of a pair of testicles attached to a large penis. To my knowledge, no-one has ever intentionally purchased one of the Red Art's paintings. They acquire a kind of semi-permanent status, hanging around for a year or so before quietly being replaced by another daub.

The Red Art staff are a motley crew of escapees from the Stans— Kazakhstan, Tajikistan, Uzbekistan, and—my personal favourite— Turkmenistan, which seems to churn out a conveyor belt of young Turk-Men who come to London, shell out 25K on an MBA at some dodgy college, then spend their entire waking lives waitering at Turkish or Kurdish kebab houses to pay off their course fees.

They all have stories to tell that make you feel you've lived your own life in a Disney movie. One of them tells me he's the sole survivor of four brothers— three of them killed by carbon monoxide poisoning from a congenitally defective gas fire installed in their family home. Every day he feels guilty he survived. Every week he sends what's left over from paying his course fees to his relatives back in Turkmenistan.

The great thing about the Red Art, in addition to its penis-lamps, is that, in contrast to the madness of the Mangal, it's usually quiet. There's no-one to disturb me in my pursuit of that Grammy I know waits just beyond the horizon. Except for the dossers. That's one of the Red Art's downsides. Especially when the weather's warm and you get a table on the street outside. Then they come swarming. There's two particular dossers with whom you might say I've built up a relationship. I don't know their real names so I call them Horace and Little Nothings. I wrote two poems about them that I intend to turn into songs.

Horace

has been blagging me for years.
Each time I step out of the bar
to spark up a smoke
he soft-shoes up the pavement
in his Oxfam overcoat.
Calls me *Uncle*.
Beams a kiss that strobes
the blackened stumps
between his lips.
Asks for twice the going rate.
I thought we were mates
until the time I open up my pockets
to display their emptiness
and he shakes those dreadnought dreadlocks
in a hump.
Calls me a *Cunt*.

Little Nothings

She mugs me coming out the Fox
in the act of shoring myself up
against a hob-nailed frost
she must have camouflaged herself
in the bus queue.
Spares me the spare-us
gets straight to the bone
asks for a fiver and I beat her down
but she clocks me staring as I
palm her a coin
while she's already
turning
to brace another mark.

It was the coat that caught me.
I was transfixed by its unravelling
as if the buffetings of wind and rain
and curses and well-meaning
had rendered it redundant
and it was sloughing off her
like spent skin to leave her
naked on the pavement.
Then she turns again to face me
and says
My life is little nothings
strung together with barbed wire
left me wondering where to find
an ATM still working at this hour.

The poems were relatively easy to write. Turning the poems into songs is a different ball game. I remember a line from the sleeve cover of one of Smokey Robinson's albums. It describes him as 'America's greatest living poet'. Apart from the fact that he's got a lot of competition in the American poetry Hall of Fame, the thing is, you can be a poet some of the time and a songwriter some of the time, but it's hard to be both all of the time. The way it works is you get an idea for the story the song's going to tell. Then you get an idea of the musical narrative.

Almost at the same time, you come up with some word sketches. Everything's disconnected. As the song develops the melody and the lyrics dance with each other until you end up with them merging together and you have a song.

Sometimes, you can start with a complete lyric—like a poem—and hitch it to a melody. But that's rare. The rhythm of the poem needs to be easily matched to the rhythm of a melody. Horace and Little Nothings didn't fit the bill. After struggling for a couple of hours trying to shoe-horn the poems into a melody, I give up. Good poems don't necessarily make good songs.

At the next rehearsal, The Manager gives us an update on responses to the mail shots. There's a letter from A&M Records. It says:

Hello.

First of all many thanks for sending your tape to us at A&M. We have listened to it thoroughly and have decided it is not what A&M are looking for on either a domestic or international basis.

However, if you have any other material please do not hesitate in submitting it to us if you feel it is strong enough for consideration.

Secondly, I must apologise for this standard letter but due to the huge volume of tapes we receive, it is impossible to write personal replies to each tape sent in.

She hasn't heard back from John Peel. Or Johnny Walker. Or Andy Kershaw.

I write a poem about the Bulger murder called 'The Ballad of Jon Alias'. It's written from the point of view of Jon Venables and imagines him doing an interview with a Tabloid journalist post parole release. There's no remorse in the poem, no justification, only the matter of fact operational details of adolescent sadism—'it wasn't like there was a script, it just spawned in our heads, like a tadpole snatching its first breath. It wasn't like skies fell in, like god came down in a chariot raining thunderbolts, it was nothing like that, I just walked home, slapped bread in the toaster'.

I want to turn it into a kind of post-punk slash-werk song for the impending apocalypse. Mad Max meets Nick Cave meets Kings of Chaos. I give Duff a sneak preview. Even Duff—consumate libertarian—is repelled by the gory details of the incomprehensibly insane revilements Venables and Thompson inflicted on poor Jamie. We can't do that mate he says shaking his head. It's way, way too hard core.

But I've become obsessed with trying to communicate the Scouse psyche in poetry and song, with its paradoxes, its stereotypes, its ridiculous contradictions. I write another poem about a Scouser who, after a night on the drugs, wakes up to find he's been transformed into his worst nightmare. I probably nicked the idea from Irvine Welsh. I'm invited to perform it at the Royal Academy of Dramatic Arts. It goes down well.

Alter Ego (A Scouser awakes)
I stir to find me arm is still asleep
it's disembodied, lying flaccid on the sheet.
The gang of navvies camped around me bed

are hammer-drilling trenches in me head.
Then I recall, in morning after fog,
shenanigans occurring down the Dog.

It's coming back now, clear as turpentine,
Big Hamish, proffering a line
as big as seven whales.
It left a blinding vapour-trail
that snaked its way round pints and nips
and then the Big Yin skips into the toilet
pulls me, helpless, in his wake,
sprays porcelain, gives himself a shake,
and, from a gaping pocket, spills
a centerfold of shiny, happy pills.
E' are son, get your laughing gear round these
he spraffs, blast guaranteed
New stuff from Poland. Only fifty pence a lid.
I knew I never should have, but I did.

It's painful getting up. I'm like a bloke
who's been left someone's body as a joke.
There's something of this gig that isn't right.
Fuck Hamish and his dodgy Polish shite,
I'm Bambi-legged. I totter to the sink,
and, poking round for something cool to drink,
confront my image in the mirror bare.
Jesus, Mary, Joseph, who's that there?
Me face is kidnapped! As I slumber,
some scally's in and done a number.
That's not my nose. It's way too wide and thick,
not like the one I used to gouge and pick.
That's someone else's gob—it's not mine either.
It's nowhere near the one that used to mither mates
But worst of all, me hair's all wrong.
It's cut and styled and straight and long.
Where once a perm my crown did top

there's now a poncey Shoreditch crop.
I've come on all distracted with the shock
and stagger to bedroom, check the clock.
I'm twenty minutes late for signing on—
open the wardrobe, find the track suit gone.
Instead of tatty trainers, there's some shoes,
a shiny, brand-new pair of Jimmy Choos.
And then, as if to underline the farce,
the pit-bull's turned around and bared its arse,
as if its never seen me face before.
I do a sharpish exit through the door
and hit the high street,
reeling from the sheer audacity of it.

Past pub and caff and betting shop
a force I'm powerless to stop
propels me by a hand unseen,
to places where I've never been.
I'm drowned in cultural pursuits
by clarinets and strings and flutes
Then in a warehouse stacked with words
I find a book, not rhyme nor verse,
but written in some foreign muck
about some radge who's woken up
to find he's got a roaches head.

The anvil drops. While in me bed,
some evil sprite has had it off.
I've turned into a raging toff.
Despondent, I'm returned to where
my violated gaff waits, stripped and bare.
Neck four temazzis, washed with foaming choc
and pray the terror's gone when I wake up.
Then in the gloom, as deathly midnight nears
a trinity of ghostly sprites appears.
The first one pulls me close and, spreading wings,

transports me high above the clouds, then brings me,
quivering with fright, to my old thatch
and shows me all the evil scams I've hatched.
The second one with sarky words and grin
most cruelly mocks the sordid state I'm in.
With sweeping gesture conjures up a scene
of all the shameful places that I've been.
Then finally, the third—the dreechest sprite—
without a word, encloaks me. I am old.
I stand in churchyard, bleak and cold
and weep in terror, beg the spirit save
my sad denuded body from the grave.

It's morning. Sunlight streams
through threadbare curtain, soothes my dreams.
Yet, mindful of the dark behind the light,
I keep my straining eye-lids watertight,
for fear a further aberration's carried out
on fizog, ear or poor mis-treated snout.
But slowly, inch by inch, the fingers creep
to where my head's protruding through the sheet.
The trembling hand connects—oh joy, oh fates!
A wiry, rampant perm luxuriates!
I'm well made up. Like Lazarus undead, spring up
and dance a jig around me bed.
And then—with warbling song and piercing cries,
I praise those kindly phantoms to the skies.
There's lessons learned from this dire visitation.
I'll pledge myself to bold renunciation
of scally deals and scheming strife.
From this day forth, I'll lead a blameless life.
And as my soul with sweet redemption fills,
resolve I'll have no more of poxy pills.

So breeze downstairs, put kettle on.
The track-suit's in its place; the Jimmies gone.

The pit-bull bares its fangs in loving grin.
I put the tatty trainers in the bin.
A brave new world of wonderment awaits.
I contemplate a visit to the Tate.
It's early doors, though.
Bags of time for art.
Then there's the weekly Quiz Night down the Dart.
I'll have a ciggie. Sit and have a think.
This new persona's thirsty work—best have a drink.
I'm staring at the clouds. It looks like rain.
Perhaps I'll take the dog—sign on again.

I convert the poem into a song concept note and distribute it at the next band rehearsal. I've scribbled some ideas on the note about how it could be done musically. In my head is a picture of Tiger Lillies and how they did those songs at the Trolley Stop that looked and felt like art installations. The idea is that the verses are all spoken word, overlaid on a bed of musical nails. Think Ian Dury— Hit me with your Rhythm Stick or Reasons to be Cheerful.

The band's reaction could charitably be described as underwhelmed. As always, Pete spearheads the dissent. "Are we doing Ken Dodd tributes now?" he sneers, depositing the crumpled up concept note unerringly into the heart of a proximate waste paper basket.

September

Never invite your band round to your own gaff. It erodes the carefully-constructed boundaries that mark your territory. Erving Goffman was right. You need to separate stage and backstage settings. If you mix them you get problems. You relax your guard. Your subordinates relax theirs. Before you know it, intimacy rears its head. Insubordination sets in.

After the success of Inga's team-bonding activity, The Manager though it would be a good idea to organise a band night out. Horrified by the potential prospect of spending an evening in a burger bar near Billericay I'd hastily offered to host it at the Mangal. We agreed on a date for the following Friday. The Mangal normally doesn't do advanced bookings but I'd milked my long-service punter credentials and managed to persuade Ali to reserve us a table. It was a smart move.

By the time we got there, the place was completely mobbed. We ordered some random starters—humus, haloumi and that spicy Turkish sausage you end up finding still lodged in your teeth the next morning—to keep us going until the special mix arrived. Then we turned our attention to the wine. Several glasses later the starters finally appeared, then swiftly disappeared.

We carried on attending to the wine. But as the interval between the despatch of the starters and the arrival of the special mix elongated into the evening, it became obvious Ali and his crew were struggling to cope. Turns out two of his waiters had been nabbed earlier in a lightning raid on the restaurant by Immigration officers and carted off.

By the time the special mixed turned up, we'd run out of our own BYOB supply and had to order more wine from the bar. By the time we got to the baklavas, I'd drunk far too much of it. If I drink too much wine, I end up ordering another bottle. I ordered two. By the time we'd finished those, I'd been spreading the love expansively, far too expansively.

"Everyone back to my place," I slur, wrapping my arms around a terrified Pete. We stagger down the street and round the corner to the house. It's encased with scaffolding the builders have erected to repair the crumbling chimney stack. Pete walks straight into it, cursing on the rebound. Duff tries a circus act launching himself onto a scaffolding pipe and immediately falling off. I manage to insert the door key on the third attempt and we all pile in. The opening door frames the cat in the hallway. It turns tail and rushes out through the cat-flap.

We go upstairs to the living room. Seduced by bonhomie I make the mistake of getting out the bottle of twelve-year-old Talisker kept for special occasions and passing it around. It's gone in sixty seconds. Max rummages in his pockets and pulls out two bags—coke and skunk. I'm delegated to roll the first spliff. My fingers don't coordinate well on account of being completely pissed so the spliff ends up looking like the last coils of a toilet roll that's been accidentally dropped in the toilet.

Reluctantly, I'm obliged to hand it back to Max. Not a good look for the band leader. Max rolls a perfect spliff. The band takes turns snorting and spliffing. I go to the CD rack and flip through the collection, decide on a classic—band leader's choice—Led Zeppelin II. The first chords of Whole Lotta Love have hardly made their way through the speakers when I hear mutterings of discontent in the background.

"It's a shit song," says Pete.

Flimsy is nodding her head in agreement.

"Any requests?" I call through the fug of skunk. It's a naive question. I get six simultaneous answers. Abdicate the DJ role. Leave them to sort it out. I need some air. I'm heading for the door when I hear Led Zeppelin replaced by Weather Girls.

Outside, it's not Raining Men but it is pissing down. I'm not used to coke and skunk combined. I experience the rain but I don't feel it. It's like I'm under an invisible umbrella. I walk down the pathway each step taking a lifetime. I experience my Self—opening its arms to embrace the rain it's not feeling. I make it to the gate. There's a figure standing there at the entrance, its own arms open wide. It's Jesus. We embrace.

Two of my bandmates rescued me half an hour later. I was sitting in the gutter with Jesus, cognitively assimilating the markings that circumscribe the parking bay. The bandmates led me inside. The interior choreographed chaos.

Discarded CDs are scattered across the floor. Crisp flakes hammered into the Turkish carpet. A wine stain slowly spreading.

My grotto—a prize collection of cod religious artefacts I've gathered on my travels and carefully curated in a corner of the living room—scattered. My favourite piece—an Our Lady of Fatima snowglobe—smashed, its snowflake liquid leaking out. Brendan is collapsed in a corner. The band ignore him. They're arguing about which sound to put on next. 3 AM. Still arguing. Finally manage to get them out of the house. I go to bed. Open the windows of the living room to let in some sanity.

I'm having a nightmare. Chased by flesh-eating zombies I run down a pathway that's full of light. But it's a dead end. I come up against a solid wall of clay. I push and push against it trying to make my way out. I wake up. It's The Manager.

"Fucking Hell," she says. "What you shoving me for?"

After the Blue Man, we'd come to the mutual conclusion that a John and Yoko would not be in the band's best interests. Yet here we were, naked, unprotected, compromised. I don't know what to do. Breakfast seems the best option.

Head pounding like an over-pumped Marshall JCM I navigate the stairs, clinging to the banister rail for support. I manage to reach the kitchen without keeling over, make my way to the espresso machine and cram two generous scoops of extra strong Illy into the portafilter. Turn around to insert the filter into the machine when I realise there isn't a machine. Instead, there's a space on the worktop that was formerly occupied by the machine.

I try to piece together the events of last night. Did I move the espresso upstairs so we wouldn't have to rouse ourselves from our drug and alcohol-induced stupor? Did I take offence at the insipid brew the machine had latterly produced and boot it out into the garden? Did Duff try to turn it into some avant-garde musical instrument?

Head swooning like a saturated sponge I spoon the coffee into a cafetiere and put some milk into a jug, turning to the microwave to heat it up. But there is only a vacant gap on the shelf where the microwave should have been. Stagger upstairs to the living room. TV gone. Hi-fi gone. Make my way to the office. The desk has been cleared. My Macintosh PowerBook gone.

I may as well have put a sign up outside the house—Burglars welcome. Free House Boot Sale. Help yourself. They'd obviously noticed the open window, shinned up the scaffolding and let themselves in. They'd probably wandered around the bedroom, noting the comatose forms stretched out on the bed, before taking their time to stroll around the house and hoover up its contents, including the vacuum cleaner.

I pour myself a coffee from the cafetiere. It tastes shit. Never use espresso coffee in a cafetiere. Fuck it. Might as well nip around to the Costa and pick up some decent espresso. I'm opening the front door and reaching for my keys hung up on a hook next to it and realise they're not there. Looking out of the half-open doorway I clock the empty parking bay that was formerly occupied by the Citroen.

The heist of the Citroen was a big loss to me. In my head, it had been the band's workhorse, its 737. Despite its compact size, you could fit most of the band's equipment in it when the back seats were down. Another plus was you didn't need to worry about an amp's sharp corner tearing the fabric or a microphone stand punching a hole in one of the seats, on account of there already being too many fabric tears and seat punctures to count.

I started to fret about how we'd get the gear to the rehearsal studio that night. Then I began the process of ringing around each member of the band to tell them the bad news. I didn't need to call Cyrus. His drum kit took up so much space he'd long ago bought a Mondeo station wagon to transport it around. So I started with Flimsy.

"No problem," she trills. "I only need to bring my voice."

Duff was his usual considerate self, sympathetic about the car theft and assuring me he'd make his own transport arrangements. Brendan sounded ecstatic. He'd bring down his gear in his new BMW. I call Pete.

"Blessing in disguise," he says. "About time you replaced that piece of shit."

I didn't bother calling Max. As I continued to ring around the band, it became obvious the band had sussed that no-one needed the Citroen except me. Everyone knew they had the means and the inclination to get themselves unaided to where they needed to be. There was no real necessity for me to pick up everyone's gear and take it to venues. My strategy of deploying the Citroen to keep the band dependent had been exposed for what it was—an instrument of control-freakery.

Two days later, I got a phone call. It was the Metropolitan Police. They'd found an abandoned car in Enfield and traced it back to me. It would be towed to their central car pound, then passed on to my insurers. A couple of days later, I got a call from the insurers. They'd inspected the Citroen and decided it was too badly-damaged to repair economically. Total write-off. They'd give me a cheque for the estimated value of the car.

After that, I could do with it as I pleased. They'd be happy to take it to the scrap yard, but if I wished I could pick it up and repair it at my own expense. I decided to pocket the money and pick it up anyway. It was at a car pound in Park Royal.

I made my way there on the Underground—an eternal twenty-two stops on the Piccadilly Line—emerging at last into the twilight of west London's industrial fart-land. The car pound was a good half mile from the tube station. By the time I got there, it was dark. I was greeted on arrival by the security guard, who looked like Bill Sykes, though more affable.

"I'll walk you to your car," he said, indicating an expanse of parked vehicles that stretched towards infinity. On the walk towards infinity, he used the time to prepare me for my reunion with the Citroen.

"If you don't mind me saying so," he began, "I think you might need to prepare yourself for a shock."

"People get very emotional about their cars," he continued. "I've seen grown men break down in tears when they see their car all mashed up."

As we press on I assure him of the equability of my temperament. Finally, we get to the last row and there's the Citroen, silhouetted against the west London gloom. Confronted by it, I spasm into an involuntary outburst, unable to contain myself. The security guard wraps a protective arm around me, then retires decorously like a funeral attendant. But what he doesn't realise is I'm laughing like a drain.

There it is—that little green Citroen AX—top of the range when I bought it a decade ago—turbo-charged; electric windows; reclining seats; reflective sun-roof—and now—amputated mirrors; headlights held on by gaffer tape; dents in the driver's door; radiator grille hanging off. Exactly the same as when it was parked outside the house a week ago. I open the front door. There, spread out on the passenger seat, is a copy of a London Evening Standard Supplement, entitled 'How to cope with car crime'.

I rock up at The Orange in the resurrected Citroen. Park it round the corner, freed from the anxiety of wondering whether there'll be another dent in it on my return. The insurance payment has made the car invincible. Though officially deceased, it's now encased in a write-off force field. I walk around the corner to The Orange.

I'm walking again in the badlands of West London. But it's posh badlands. Kensington borders. Serious money. Yuppies snaffling at the trough. Upward mobility. Crippling mortgage payments. Granola and decaffeinated Colombian for breakfast. The performance contract The Manager had to sign goes with the territory. Pure naked capitalism.

The Orange management bears no responsibility for any losses the artist(s) incur (insert name of artist(s) here).

The contract stipulates we need to shift a minimum of forty tickets ourselves to get paid anything. We get £1 per ticket sold. We get nothing for any punters who come in from the street. The upside is The Orange is a serious venue. It's got a dressing room for the 'performing artists' and it's got heavy-duty equipment. Soundtracs 24:4:2 desk. 4 wedge PA. Yamaha Q2031A Full High Definition monitor. Everything was set up to accelerate our progress along Tin Pan Alley.

But we're deep in bandit territory. Out of our local comfort zone. The support act is a band called Mariposa. I'm not sure if it's called after the Spanish for butterfly or after the Canadian folk music festival. Either epithet would fit. They look and sound a bit lightweight. A tad breathless. They do a few numbers you'd be hard-pressed to remember. All pan pipes and Aztec tequila sunrise. It leaves the audience unedified. We go on stage to a wall of indifference. Well, fuck yer indifference, ya muppets.

I'd deliberately chosen The Orange to take us out of our comfort zone. I'd chosen it to unleash my latest musical assault on the world, an RPG fired into the marketplace—the long-gestating but finally completed 'Desperate, Lonely, Suicidal?' The question mark is interrogative rather than declarative, the tone is ironic rather than evangelical. It's 4/4 with a ridiculously quick beat—208 BPM. The verses are just two chords—A ♭ m, G ♭ m:

Looking in the mirror there
Don't like your face don't like your hair
Who is that monster staring back
Your chin's too sharp your jaw too slack
No sex no drugs no rock and roll
Can pacify your aching soul

You want to be somebody else
Why don't you recreate yourself
Looking in the mirror there
The TV's told you what to wear
But everything about you's wrong
Your skirt's too short
Your legs too long
Desperate lonely suicidal
'cos you don't look like Billy Idol
your life's a drag
you hate yourself
Why don't you recreate yourself

Then the chorus comes in descending from G flat through Em to E, ending with the last line on G ♭:

It's your story
You don't have to take it any more
What's your hurry
You can throw it all away
Do something that you never did before

The middle eight is pure scat vocal with Flimsy improvising to a background composed entirely of snare drum:

Looking in the mirror there
You hate your shabby underwear
You've had your time
You've done your best
You failed the swimming costume test
Your days are short
Your nights are long
Your ego's weak
Your perfume's strong
You're living at the wrong address
Why don't you recreate yourself
Recreate yourself

It's driven by a relentless glam rock bass and rhythm guitar line I think I lifted from Mud's 'Tiger Feet'. The middle eight isn't a middle eight at all. The whole song completely suspends itself and there's pure silence, creating a space for Flimsy's scat-improvisation—doo waab doo waab doo waab baby mamma mama momma yeah yeah. There's no sax in the song. Just grunge guitar and Hammond keyboard. When I first introduced it at rehearsal, I knew the band knew it was a potential numero uno. The hook song that would get the record companies sitting up and begging.

I put it down on The Orange set list as the penultimate number—the one before we do Temple of Love as the finale. It was a bad decision. I should have switched the songs around. 'Desperate Lonely' went down a storm. Wide boys pogoing around the dance floor. Yuppy heads swaying berserkly in time to its bonkers beat. Mariposa looking on enviously as we sucked in the audience and spat it out. 'Temple of Love' turned out to be an anti-climax. To be honest, I'd always hated it, even though I'd spawned it.

The after-gig is always an anti-climax. You're still gig-surfing, riding the adrenalin wave when you come off stage. You have a couple of drinks then you pack up the gear. The adrenalin's tamped down a touch, but you're still enervated. You get in the car and you're still enervated. Driving back along the Westway with The Manager in the passenger seat. Absorbing the sound of tyres on the tarmac, the solidity of silent office blocks that tower above us as we swish past.

I want to tune into the metronomic swish of the tyres, the comforting solidity of those grey shapes. But The Manager is too enervated. She's still gig-surfing. The second set was brilliant she gushes especially 'Desperate' but you should give it more animation you need to crank up your stage presence on that one give it a bit more physical movement. I'm grunting agreement hoping that will stop the gush but all the time I'm trying to tune it out. We're heading inexorably towards the outer suburbs of the capital. Towards another John and Yoko.

We wake up the next morning to find two letters have dropped onto the doormat. The Manager opens them up as we're having a spartan breakfast of Weetabix and toast, her kids watching sullenly as they prepare for the torture of school. The first letter is from Virgin Records. It says:

Thank for sending in your material, which has been listened to.

Unfortunately, we do not feel it is suitable for Virgin at this time, however, thank you for letting us hear it and I wish you good luck with the idea.

The second is from Phonogram. It says:

Many thanks for sending us your demo tape.

I have listened to it carefully and after careful consideration have decided to pass.

I appreciate the trouble and effort you went to in putting this together and unfortunately I cannot go through a detailed account as to why I came to my decision.

I do hope you will continue in your efforts of writing and recording and will bear us in mind for any future material you may have.

Looking across the breakfast table at The Manager's kids an image of limpets springs to mind. They're sucking the life out of her. You can literally see the effects in the way her cheekbones get more prominent day by day. It's as if the sub-stratum tissue is continually being absorbed and broken down, then sublimated into a kind of vapourised nectar the kids suckle on.

Then there's the attrition in the atmosphere they suckle on. It's like the house is a tiny castle under medieval siege, bombarded by the artillery of the Department of Social Security, the Local Education Authority and various credit card companies. There's too many bills and not enough money coming in. The gutters need replacing. The radiators need bleeding. The Manager counterattacks the siege. Puts all her considerable resources into pushing it back. But she's on her own. It's a constant, sapping struggle.

She's assembled an arsenal of weapons for the struggle. She's appropriated Buddhist philosophy. Add your light to the sum of lights. Karma will bring its reward. She's adopted meditative practices. Then there's the accoutrements. Aromatic tea lights. Nag Champa incense. The nightly spliff after the kids have gone to bed. And there's the band. The band is the walkway that carries her across the gorge and the swirling whirlpools that lie beneath. The band is the veneer of glamour that glosses over the crushed cornflakes, the embarrassing parents' evenings, the clapped-out Astra that refuses to start in the morning.

I'll drop the kids off at school and then we can talk about the letters The Manager says. I wave goodbye to her catatonic offspring as they shuffle off to the Astra. Clock the extenuated coughing and wheezing before it stutters into life then disappears up the road.

The vacated space allows me an opportunity to appraise the situation. I can't help thinking it's not only a bit cliched but that the cliche is a tad sordid. It's good copy doing a John and Yoko if you live on Fifth Avenue. It's less appealing if you're sitting in a council flat in the boonies of Outer London. I come to a decision. It's time for a parting of the ways. It's regrettable but good for the band. And for me. And for her.

I register the click of the door latch. She comes into the kitchen smiling that big toothy smile.

"Sorry, it took so long," she says. "The head teacher mugged me about the parents evening." Then she clocks my granite gaze. "Are you OK?" she asks.

"I'm fine," I say. "But we need to talk about the future."

She slides onto a breakfast stool. "Every time I hear someone say we need to talk about the future," she says, "I know we're talking about the past. So let's just skip the crap. There's only one question. Are you with me or are you not?"

She's framed in the doorway as I make my exit. The doorway itself framed by the human touches she'd applied to soften its brutalism—the pot plants placed on either side of the entrance, the fairy lights tracing its periphery. She's wearing a pair of torn jeans that reinforce the impression of damage incurred—the collateral of daily struggle against the bum hand she'd been dealt.

I suddenly see myself as I am—the latest disappointer in a long line of disappointments. I'll call you I say as I turn on my heel, kicking away the kiddie bike that blocks my path. I make it to the Citroen. Open the door. Turn the key in the ignition, It starts first time.

My tribe was a big fan of religion. Religion is a powerful reinforcer of stuckness. It works to keep people in line, so they don't stray too far from the prescribed path. It provides a convenient way of encouraging people to avoid taking responsibility for changing their lives, by offering them miracles— including salvation, the ultimate miracle. I'm the great-grandson of a miracle— though not an official one.

My great grandfather—Jack—is one of five thousand medical cures for which the Lourdes Medical Bureau can find no natural or scientific explanation. Jack was a soldier in the Royal Marines. In various military actions—at Antwerp;

in Egypt and at Gallipoli—he suffered wounds that led to a set of impediments any Scouser would love to display on their disability allowance application—including paralysis of the arm, partial paralysis of the legs and epilepsy.

As a result of a number of medical operations, including brain surgery to remove shrapnel, he was discharged from military service and given the Scouse dream—a one hundred per cent disability pension. Back in Liverpool, he spent most of the time in his wheelchair or in bed.

In July 1923, he heard a pilgrimage to Lourdes was being organised. He took a gold sovereign he'd saved for an emergency that hadn't already been nicked and used it as the down payment on a ticket. His family and friends thought he was bonkers to even think about going. His doctor told him the journey would be suicide. But Jack was determined to go.

Even for the able-bodied, the pilgrimage to Lourdes in those days was a nightmare. My great-grandfather was very ill en route and after finally arriving in Lourdes he had several haemorrhages and epileptic fits. During his six days there he took a punt in the water from the Lourdes grotto nine times and attended all the ceremonies they arranged for sick people on their last legs.

On the afternoon of 25 July 1923, the miracle started. In his own words, as he was being blessed by the Archbishop of Rheims, his right arm became agitated and burst its bandages. So, he grabbed the spotlight from the Archbishop and blessed himself. Later that night, he suddenly jumped out of his sick bed; made a dash for the door and ran towards the Lourdes Grotto, about three hundred yards away—the first time he was able to get out of bed in years.

On his return to Liverpool, he started a haulage business, humping two hundred pound sacks of coal up narrow tenement stairways, right up until the time he died in 1943. The available evidence suggests that, apart from slight muscle wastage in the right arm, he showed no signs of his former condition.

The three doctors who had examined him prior to his journey to Lourdes re-examined him. Their signed statement testified that he could walk perfectly; that he had recovered the use and function of his right arm; that he had regained sensation in his legs; and finally, that the opening in his skull made by the brain surgery had vanished.

When I was about eight or nine, my grandmother took me on a pilgrimage to Lourdes, re-tracing Jack's footsteps. I was an anxious pilgrim. Religion scared me. Travel scared me. My grandmother scared me. My grandmother's sitting room scared me. It housed a long sideboard on which was arraigned a display of glass jars in which shapeless nameless things drifted slowly in fluid, like dead babies.

The thing I remember most about the pilgrimage was the swarm of flies that settled in my ears, eyes and mouth. They were particularly drawn to the Pyrenean donkeys I was forced to mount so we could plod up the sharp inclines of the mountains. Lourdes itself was penitents and relic-peddlers; plastic miracle-tubes—holy water in small, medium and large, screw-topped with the head of the Virgin. I wondered whether these different sizes produced small, medium or large miracles.

The hotel we stayed in was grand but small, faded and bourgeois. It was situated near the Grotto. I remember the smell of spinach and watercress soup; the chimes of the Basilica that rang the hours and half hours through the night, playing *Ave Maria*. There was a bathing house close to the Grotto. Water was piped to it from the spring where the Virgin Mary is claimed to have appeared to Bernadette Soubirous in 1858.

Hundreds of penitents and suppliants queue up to bathe in its curative waters, many of them incurables in the last chance saloon. My grandmother insisted I queue up with them. The pool had handrails for the disabled. Irreverently, I remembered the old joke about the wheelchair that went into the pool and came out with its tires re-treaded. My grandmother gesticulated impatiently, "Get in the pool."

I was terrified. What if someone with leprosy or impetigo had just been in there? I clung to the handrail and whimpered. Stuck again.

The abiding regret in our family is that my great-grandfather didn't make the uber-cure list—the sixty-two cures that have been officially declared miraculous. They shouldn't feel so bad. It's a painfully tortuous process, joining the ranks of illustrious medical conundrums like Clementine Trouve, Marie-Therese Canin and Leo Schwager.

First, you have to lodge your claim with the Medical Bureau. Then the claim is subjected to the scrutiny of medical professionals. This considerably reduces your chances, since any doctor in the world is eligible to scrutinise. If the Bureau is satisfied, the cure appears to be genuine at the end of a second investigation (at least twelve months after the first) the case is then referred to the Medical Commission in Paris.

The Commission makes a thorough study of the documents, certificates, results of examinations, x-rays, lab tests and other evidence related to the case.

The Commission calls in whatever specialists it considers necessary. After this examination, the Commission rejects the cure or accepts it. If accepted, the cure is then sent on to the bishop of the diocese in which the would-be miracle lives, with the recommendation that a Canonical Commission is appointed to investigate it. So it's the Church that makes the decision whether to upgrade a cure to the status of a miracle.

This is what scuppered Jack's chances. It was the Church. The fact is miracles have a strong Gallic bias. If you look at the sixty-two cures with the Vatican seal of approval, fifty-seven come from France. There's one Belgian, one Spanish, one Italian, one Swiss and one Austrian. No British. And certainly no Scouser. Where is Lourdes? And where is the Medical Bureau situated? You get the picture. It's a bit like UEFA when Liverpool teams always get the group of death. Or the European Commission, when the French always veto Scouse initiatives.

The other thing is that all the official miracles involve clerics. The list is full of Brothers, Sisters, Fathers and acolytes, although the odd agricultural worker does get a mention. But no coalmen. I also suspect my great-grandfather's miracle stretched credibility even by Lourdes's standards. If you look at the list, a lot of miracles involve cures that are conveniently hidden, like tuberculosis and fistulas. His cure involved the disappearance of a giant hole in the head and a gold plate.

Other miracles look like cures the average GP surgery could easily rustle up. Cases like Antonia Moulin—suppurating wound of the right foot—or Pierre de Rudder—open fracture of the leg. My great grandfather's cure was just too hardcore; too bold; too *scally* to handle. We were stuck again, this time in the miracle queue.

October

I turn up for rehearsal without The Manager. Hawk-eye Pete is the first to notice.

"Where's the Manager," he demands as I sidle solo into the studio.

"The Manager is gone," I respond. "Der Manager ist nicht mehr."

"Why?" he asks.

"We realised we had musical indifferences," I reply. "Our aesthetic trajectories converged to a point where they became too compatible. So in the interests of the collective good, she decided to fuck off."

"We don't need a manager," I continue. "We're quite capable of managing gigs ourselves. And anyway, she wasn't great at managing. Remember Harry Hazell?"

The mention of the name brings a shiver into the studio as if I'd blurted out the title of The Scottish Play in front of a bunch of thespians. Duff quivers as he re-lives the shame. "It's like PTSD," he says.

"Yeah—and there were loads of other fuck-ups," Flimsy chips in. "Like that huge bar bill for those chancers at the Rock Garden. The cod A&R men."

"She was really lovely though," says Max. Brendan nods his head in assent. "And a really good laugh too."

I need to get a grip on this sentimental wallowing. We need to forge on. Semper prorsum.

"I know, I know," I shout waving my arms like a distracted farmyard hen. "She *was* lovely. She *was* a good laugh. She hooted like a turbo-charged donkey. But she couldn't manage a fucking car boot sale. Let's move on. As of now, *I'm* managing the band. I get the gigs. I tell you where they are. I tell you when to turn up. OK?"

They're looking dubious, but they're not looking rebellious. "We're under new management," I say trying to sound authoritative. "And it starts with a really massive gig this weekend."

The Mean Fiddler. Harlseden. It used to be a boxing club. Until Vince Power got hold of it and turned it into a musical lodestone. Vince Power, IBMG. Irish Boy Made Good. According to his cv, he escaped the Waterford bogs and arrived in London with nothing but a giant pair of hands and an even bigger work ethic. Signed up on the Lump and laboured on building sites, graduating to demolition before diverting into house clearances.

There he discovered the discreet charm of furniture and its sell-on potential. Set up a string of second-hand shops around northwest London. Made a fortune. Invested it in nightclubs, restaurants, music venues and festivals. The Mean Fiddler was one of his first music enterprises. In the early days, it served as a tabernacle to his own tastes. Like you've bought a giant living room and invited all your favourite records to perform in it live. So it started off with country and western and boyos from the Emerald Isle. But Vince's special talent for promotion grabbed it like the jaws of a JCB and dropped it onto the main stage.

He enticed Johnny Cash to appear. Roy Orbison played his last UK gig there in 1987. Neil Young turned up. Paul McCartney dropped in. The Fiddler kick-started the careers of Van Morrison and The Pogues. There's a cast list of players that send a shiver down your musical spine. John Martyn, Eric Clapton, Nick Cave, Jon Mayall, The Specials, Black Crowes, Billy Bragg, Bhundu Boys and—Half Man Half Biscuit.

They came from the wrong side of the Mersey but I'd long ago forgiven them. I'd played 'Back Again in the DHSS' so many times I'd had to change the stylus on the record player. Every time I played it, I was left with a deep sense of inadequacy. How could I possibly top a song like 'The Bastard Son of Dean Friedman'?

We turn up at The Fiddler in a snowstorm, an unseasonal Atlantic depression depositing five centimetres onto an unprepared Harlesden. Most venues we'd be coping with the aftermath by shivering in the toilets, changing into dry gear whilst trying to avoid the piss puddles on the floor. But the Fiddler embraces us with warm open arms, inviting us into a changing area that wouldn't be out of place at a Premier League club.

There's three shower enclosures with thermostatic individual diverters and a chill-out space with reclining couches. The band wander around the dressing room like hostages released into a rehabilitation facility. Pete turns on a shower tap. Brendan stretches out on a bench. Flimsy prods a reclining couch. Don't get too comfortable, I warn, in my new managerial tone. Let's get focused on the gig.

After the storming response to 'Desperate, Lonely, Suicidal?' at The Orange, I'd retained the same set list for the Mean Fiddler, but with 'Desperate' slated as the final song, after Temple of Love and its obligatory band introductions.

I put Fire on Ice into the set before Desperate to build up the momentum. It's a bit of a banger like Desperate but more pared down and laid back. Starts with a thudding 4 bar bass line followed by 4 bars of slashing guitar chords—just two of them—Gbm then E—before I come in on verse one, same chords:

Out of the dark times
Must come the good
Life turns a corner
Just like I knew it would.

Verse two is a variation on the Gbm theme for the first two lines before sliding into E, D and E on the last two:

I was walking on quicksand
Sinking slowly out of sight
I was out in the pouring rain
Then the sun came up shining bright.

The chorus is just a simple up-down discourse between D and E with a sneaky Gb thrown in on the third bar of the last line to keep people awake:

Vision of Angels
Fire on ice
Out of the dark
And into the light.

We repeat the verse two structure:

I was heading on down that road
Hard on my heels the dogs of fear
Chained up inside that cage
Shouting so loud no-one is ever gonna hear.

Then slip into the chorus again:

Vision of Angels
Fire on ice
Out of the dark
And into the light.

The middle eight is pure guitar solo. It's a challenge for Pete. Not naturally a head banger he's used to delicate, one might call them fussy, jazz arpeggios so he takes on the eight bars of Jimmy Page style rock improvisation more with grim determination than enthusiasm.

We repeat verse one and wind the song up with sixteen bars of prolonged last line repetition and slash guitar.

I guess I expected the same audience response as the one at The Orange. But as we go through the set it becomes obvious The Fiddler is a dead audience. There's no buzz. No spark.

If it had been a blind date I'd have woken up the next morning thinking it hadn't been a disaster but I wouldn't be holding my breath waiting for a phone call. It underlines the cliche that you're only as good as your last gig. I'd been seduced into thinking that because we'd graduated to a tier above the Bangers and Mash venues our progression up the greasy pole was assured. But we might as well have been playing in the local youth club. No-one in The Fiddler audience was interested.

The Fiddler was a salutary lesson in music-biz realpolitik. The London B-list circuit revealed itself for what it was. An endless washing machine where you get churned around and end up in the same place you'd started from. I began to think we needed new horizons. I started to lay the foundations for a European tour. Something to get us noticed beyond the incestuous dog eat dog of the London circuit.

I put out feelers to friends in Amsterdam, Paris, Berlin, Madrid and Milan. They feed me some scraps. But you still have to put in the hard yards. I compile a list of promoters, influencers, venue managers, publicists and send them the revised press pack and the CD. I wait for the response. Nada. Niente. Rien. Niets. Gar Nichts.

As the responses fail to arrive I realise I'm an Orientalist. My assumption was that in the backwaters of Europe, they're desperate to open their arms to anything that has a London label. What I didn't understand because I'm an Orientalist is that every big city on the Continent has the same music ecosystem. All of the bands in Amsterdam, Paris, Berlin, Madrid and Milan are working to the same rules we're working within London. Dog eat dog. Why would they want to book a band that only a few people in Dalston have heard of? I realise we need an angle. We need a bandwagon. Then the bandwagon revealed itself.

HIV. The rates were continuing to climb. The big moral panic about the 'gay plague' became exposed for what it was—a big moral panic. Heterosexual transmission was accelerating beyond non-heterosexual transmission. The public health message—Just Say NO—was exposed as the usual government guff. Public health information was all wrong. It was clunky, panicky and, ultimately, useless.

In my day job researching how transmission worked, it became obvious you needed messaging targeted at different lifestyles, different cultures, different beliefs. I know what you're thinking. How can you possibly contemplate taking advantage of a brutal pandemic that was cutting short the lives of millions of people, particularly young people. But in my book, you need to capitalise on a crisis. Maximise its opportunities.

And in any case, the logic of doing an HIV tour was inescapable. We take the safer sex message out on the streets. We take it into the clubs. We make it accessible. We make it fun.

So, I blagged the Barcelona Tour. The launch pad was a European project I'd been working on in HIV prevention. It had some powerful partners— including a major Spanish telecoms company. All the corporates in the world were falling over themselves to demonstrate they were contributing to the Fight Against AIDS.

I arranged a meeting with the telecoms company. Suggested it wouldn't look good if they were seen to be doing less than their competitors in the FAA. Pitched them a proposal to bankroll an innovative public health initiative that would take the safer sex message onto the streets and into the clubs. And, given the pressing nature of the AIDS crisis and the need to do something as quickly as possible, I was willing to offer the services of my band in order to cut bureaucratic corners and deliver the message rapido.

They see the inherent logic of my synopsis. They make me an offer. The !Consciente del SIDA! tour. Sponsored by the company. All expenses paid, subject to compliance with company regulations. The company's extensive communications, publicity and advertising resources are at the disposal of the band. Rock and Roll. We're on.

I start to plan the tour. Realise we'll be navigating territory even more unknown than the Badlands of West London. Realise I need to beef up the posse. We're on a tight budget. The telecoms company have set clear boundaries on what they're prepared to grease. I need a support act. I need a gopher. But I need cheap.

For the support act the obvious choice was a solo artist. And you couldn't get a cheaper solo artist than my nephew. He'll be ecstatic just at the prospect of a trip abroad. A few quid in his pocket for expenses and he'll be rolling over like a puppy. He's completely unknown and his career won't suffer a set-back in the event the tour turns out bad. For the gopher, it's a no-brainer. Porno Dave. Dave will go anywhere if there's a sniff of sex, drugs and rock and roll. The big challenge is to sell it to the band. It's difficult enough to get them to move beyond the North Circular, let alone a different country.

I announce the !Consciente del SIDA! tour to an unsuspecting band at the next rehearsal. It's a classic London autumnal evening and the rain is hammering down on the studio roof. Like Thomas Hardy in Tess of the D'Urbevilles, I use the weather to camouflage my ulterior motives. Minging weather I offer casually as the band are setting up.

Duff is the first to respond. "Yeah," he acknowledges. "Wish we were rehearsing somewhere else. Somewhere warmer than this shit-hole." I can't believe I've been handed at the very first gambit the opening I'd expected to be grafting hard for. But carpe diem.

"It's funny you should say that," I respond. "I've been thinking the same thing myself. Playing somewhere more exotic. Like Brazil. Or the Seychelles. Or even Spain."

The rest of the band has been picking up on the conversation.

"Let's go home," says Max. "We're guaranteed a warm welcome in my country."

"Yeah," retorts Pete. "An AK-47 warm welcome."

Max acknowledges the truth of the remark with an ironic grimace.

"I wouldn't mind Spain," says Flimsy lowering the mic stand to her diminutive level. "Sand. Sangria. Sex."

Max visibly flinches.

"It's funny you should say that," I chime in. "I've been given a tug by some people about doing some gigs in Spain."

Pete's ears prick up. "What people?"

"Well, there's a few promoters who contacted me who are working with some politicians on the AIDS problem," I say. Now I've definitely got the band's attention. They're giving out mixed vibes of interest, puzzlement and apprehension.

"What's AIDS got to do with it," asks Pete sounding like a punk version of Tina Turner.

I spin him the well-rehearsed spiel.

"Governments have got it all wrong about how to stop the spread of HIV," I explain—"especially our government. But the Spanish are more progressive. They realise you need to stop lecturing young people on how to behave. They've come up with an idea to spread the message about safer sex through music. So, they've got together with a bunch of music promoters to get some bands to do some Safer Sex gigs."

"Why us," asks Pete suspiciously. "Why don't they use their own bands?"

I free-fall bullshit. "Well, the progressive governments think the message will be stronger if it's a multi-national and a multi-cultural message. They want to bring English bands to Spain to work with the local ones."

"So, why don't they ask the Stones," says Pete.

"Because one, they can't afford it and two, they want a band that's fresh off the streets," I respond. "One that normal kids can identify with."

I can see I've got their interest. A few questions are haltingly posed, then they come in thick and fast, stacking up like planes on the Heathrow glide path.

Pete—Who's organising the tour?

Max—Where are we staying?

Flimsy—Do I get my own room?

Pete—Who's managing the tour?

Brendan—How many gigs are we playing?

Pete—Are we guaranteed payment?

Cyrus—Can I bring my own drum kit?

Duff—Do we get any free drugs?

Brendan—How long are we on tour?

Duff—What kind of drugs will we get?

I lie fluently throughout the interrogation. Eventually, the band falls silent. It looks like !Consciente del SIDA! could be a goer.

"How much do we get paid?" asks Max.

I quote a figure.

"When do we start," he says.

In the aftermath of the Hylde-moðer disaster, I kept my head down. Having escaped relatively lightly, with a verbal warning from the police, I applied myself to more acceptable forms of self-advancement in order to combat the purgatory of stuckness.

I found something almost Tantric in the discipline of the curriculum. The rhythms and cadences of quadratic equations soothed and beguiled. As if by osmosis, I drew strength from the elegant symmetry of the periodic table of the elements. In geomorphology, I stood on the summits of towering mountain ranges and marvelled at the sheer effrontery of glaciers and calderas.

For my second act of rebellion, I switched compulsions. The Hylde-moðer debacle had dampened my lust for the flame. I turned instead to eleutheromania. Eleutheromania presents itself clinically as an obsessive desire for freedom. Since the condition is rare, there are few examples on record of how it works. Most of these feature incarcerated desperados who endlessly repeat ill-conceived, ineffective and ultimately futile attempts to escape.

I took the opposite approach. Instead of breaking out of the education system, I mounted a series of ill-conceived, ineffective and increasingly futile break-ins. The break-ins, I reasoned, would liberate me from stuckness by striking a blow against one of the main things that kept me stuck—the school.

The first break-in involved another scaling of the school gates—this time on a wet Sunday morning. The buildings looked deserted. Preliminary reconnaissance revealed a convenient point of entry. The outside door to the caretaker's office was unlocked, but a careful peek confirmed the absence of a caretaker. The table inside hosted a copy of a tabloid, open at the Sports Section; a half-consumed mug of pale tea and the crust of a bacon sandwich. I checked the corridor outside. It gaped passively back at me. I mounted the stairs and headed for the laboratory. This too was unlocked.

Entering a forbidden space is one of the most pervasive human taboos. In Medieval times, in certain areas, protocols were invoked that stipulated an invading army must give notice of its imminent invasion of an opponent's territory. Vampires are expressly forbidden to cross the threshold of a dwelling unless invited to do so.

So, invading forbidden space is both scary and exhilarating. If you do it, you have to do it with panache. It is said that some housebreakers leave excrement in their victims' dwellings not because fear of detection has loosened their bowels but because they like to leave their own particular calling-card as evidence of their transgression.

The laboratories in the school were demarcated according to the Biglan model—hard versus soft, pure versus applied, life versus nonlife. There was one for physics; one for chemistry and one for biology. But which one would offer the most elegant calling card? A weight of indecision sandbagged my resolve. There they were again. The three stooges—choice, procrastination and stuckness, mocking from the shadows.

It was time to make a statement. I evaluated the options. Physics seemed the least promising of the three. On the plus side, its laboratory, with its van der graf generators; microscopes and voltmeters, housed a catalogue of destructible hardware. Any of these items, cast violently to the floor, would produce an impressive fallout of collapsed metal and showered glass. Yet, these artefacts seemed somehow unappealing. Physics was too prosaic; too journeyman. It lacked nobility. My compulsion was underscored by liberation, not destruction.

Chemistry had a more compelling allure. I had already accumulated not inconsiderable skills in alchemy. Assisted by habitues of the Hylde-moðer smoking club, I had collaborated in experiments aimed at opening up the narco-pharmacology envelope. In nondescript parents' garages, we blended combinations of anaesthetics. We discovered that a mixture of ACE—alcohol, chloroform and ether—in a 5:1:1 ratio, produced a neurochemical effect ten times as powerful and long-lasting as that of cleaning fluid, give or take a couple of standard deviations.

The alpha trial of ACE was conducted in Big Malc's garage, whilst his parents were on vacation in Majorca. The results were encouraging. Out of nine volunteers, only two were hospitalised. But the purists amongst us demanded refinements. ACE went back to the garage. It emerged sleeker; more streamlined. Less chloroform. More alcohol. The Beta trial involved around a hundred Northern Soul freaks and a deserted warehouse near Wigan railway station. ACE had to compete with brown bombers, black beauties, dexies, blow, dots and jellies. It won hands down. It was considerably more cost-effective.

But the problem with chemistry was that it was just too attractive. Behind those bland doors, a lapdance of caustics, bromides, nitrates and heavy metals arched itself. I had already got my fingers burned with the Hylde-moðer. Further pyrotechnics were too risky. It had to be biology. I had no innate fondness for the subject. It wasn't just that its Head of Department had the face of a small pumpkin and a voice that could shear tungsten. It was all that gratuitous butchery of small animals.

I recently came across an article on the web on dissecting frogs, written by a teacher based in California. In slightly peeved mode, she states, "For a variety of reasons, a handful of students in my class do not choose to dissect frogs with the class during the regular class session." It was only fitting that biology should take a central stage in my war of stuckness liberation.

I sauntered into the biology lab clad in the protective suit of a liberationist. There were rows of cages arranged along the windows that backed onto the playing field. I opened the windows. Then I opened one cage containing locusts and another cage that contained three rabbits. The locusts seized the opportunity to fly straight out to freedom. The rabbits were less forthcoming. They seemed happy in their captivity. I waved a few lettuce leaves in their direction, but they stayed put.

I picked up one rabbit and moved it towards the window but it sank its teeth into my thumb. I decided to leave the rabbits to ponder their existential choices without human intervention. On my way out of the school, I upturned two benches and tipped them into the goldfish pond, oblivious to the fact that I'd liberated a species used to desert temperatures into a dank English autumnal afternoon and consigned a bunch of rabbits to almost certain myxomatosis.

November

Touch down at El Prat in a snowstorm. Pete's head torched with images of Munich and the Busby Babes as the plane comes in low over the water. The arrivals hall teeming with colliding stag and hen night parties from Bradford and Manchester.

There's carnage on the dance floor. Pete thinks of Freddie Mercury—Freddie had no idea when he penned that Olympic dirge. Barcelona! It's a shithole. There's a problem with the luggage. Cyrus's drums fail to appear on the carousel. The lead singer tries to sort it out. Usual faffing about. Eventually, it's established the kit's been impounded by Spanish customs. They're doing a thorough search for drugs, unaware that Cyrus sees his body as a temple and wouldn't touch a spliff even if God passed it around.

The band need to hang around while they do it. Pete can't help thinking this fuck-up is the lead singer's fault. After he'd dumped the manager he'd had to take the band management on board himself. The manager would have sorted the problem in no time. Or it would never have happened. But the lead singer's got no clue. What really pisses Pete off is the nepotism. The lead singer's packed the tour with hangers on. His mate Dave—the alleged graphic artist who did the cover for the CD. What's he here for? His nephew's been signed up as the warm-up act—never had a shave by the look of him.

The band heads to the souvenir shop to kill some time while the drugs search is going on. Flimsy buys a tee shirt with 'GO BARCA!' stencilled across the front. The lead singer gets something for his home grotto. It's one of those plastic things shaped like an igloo. When you turn it upside down it shakes up a snowstorm that settles to reveal a miniature Gaudi cathedral.

After a couple of hours, they reluctantly release Cyrus's kit. The band go out to the car park to look for the van the lead singer has hired. It's not hard to locate. It's the one that looks like it's come from Trotter's Independent Traders. It's already been ticketed for parking violations when the band gets to it. There's no driver.

Apparently, there's been a misunderstanding. The lead singer thought he was renting a vehicle with a driver. The rental company thinks it's renting out a vehicle that's driven by the renter. There's a band discussion on the forecourt, punctuated by traffic police trying to move the band on. Max is the only one with a licence that doesn't have penalty points. He becomes the designated driver.

The band throw the gear into the back and head out towards the city. Arrive at the hotel two hours later after several circumnavigations around the Diagonal. When they check in, it's like an away match in the Doc Martens League. To save money the lead singer has gone and booked twin rooms for the band—except for himself and Flimsy who, in a sop to decorum, has been given her own room. Max's not happy. Pete's not happy. He's bunking with Brendan.

The band go out for dinner together at Les Quinze Nits—a big restaurant in Placa Real, just off La Rambla—the place where all the tourists go. The band gets its own table upstairs, away from the tourists. Pete registers the waiters. They all seem to be from China. Perhaps, he thinks, Mao sent spare comrades from the Long March to reinforce the International Brigade in the Spanish Civil War and they settled here.

He orders a starter of poularde cannelloni with Trumpets of Death followed by seafood paella. The cannelloni tastes like shredded wheat left soaking too long in Oxo. At least the Trumpets of Death taste like mushrooms. The paella is so stodgy he could use it to re-glue the lino in the hotel bathroom. Luckily they've got gallons of Sangria to wash it all down.

They stagger out of Les Quinze Nits to the Glacier Bar at the corner of Placa Real. Colonise a cluster of outside tables on the square, all empty because it's still freezing. At the adjacent table, a couple of junkies are gouging on heroin, oblivious to the temperature. They drink more Sangria. Stagger across the square to Carrer dels Escudellers and come across a bar in Placa de George Orwell. Order more Sangria.

Drink a toast to the man who predicted Margaret Thatcher. Re-trace their steps along Carrer dels Escudellers and end up at a heavy metal karaoke dive called Haven. Drink more Sangria with Fundador chasers. Pete clocks the lead singer scrabbling on stage. He delivers a pitiful version of Street Fighting Man. Pete wishes he had his guitar with him. Wishes he was back with Shire Draits.

Can't remember how he got back to the hotel. Wakes up at five am with Brendan's snores clanging in his ears.

To start the tour the band is back in Placa Real, at a bar called Sidecar. The stage is usually occupied by a big screen, where they show televised football. They fold up the screen and pack it away for live music. So the band has to fit into the space where the screen had been. Pete's not happy with the arrangements.

The punters are really in his face. He thinks they're likely to get up for a piss when he's in the middle of a solo. The lead singer's nephew goes on first. Pete thinks he looks like he's just finished a shift picking turnips off a field in the Norfolk Broads. But he admits to himself the nephew's not bad. Good guitar technique. Knows his way around the frets. Voice OK too. Gets the punters interested.

The nephew finishes with an acoustic version of Hendrix's All along the Watchtower—which Pete wouldn't attempt in a month of Sundays. But the Catalans seem to like it. Give him an enthusiastic round of applause. He's followed by a local band called Little Red Roosters. They do covers. Crowd-pleasers that get the punters nodding their heads. The band is very tight and organised. Good stage presence.

The nephew and the support band warm the audience up nicely. The band go on stage to another round of applause as the punters catch sight of Flimsy's GO BARCA! tee shirt. *She's such a fucking crowd-sponge*, thinks Pete. *Always desperate to suck in adulation.*

The band start a bit shaky, as you would expect on a first night. Cyrus is waywardly setting the pace. His timing is all over the place. The band follow cue. Brendan's dropping notes like a demented geriatric knitting tea-cosies in a care home. Max's farting riffs way out of time. The keyboard's pinging. The lead singer's totally off key. The band don't really recover. But the audience doesn't seem to mind. They're all pissed. It's gone quite well for an opening gig. Roll on La Boite.

Pete had been looking forward to La Boite after the beer and fags stint at Sidecar. It's a serious jazz venue. He and Cyrus are the only ones in the band with jazz credentials. He could tell the lead singer was intimidated by the seriousness of it. How the muppet managed to get 477 Avenue Diagonal is a mystery to Pete. He could see the lead singer was dead nervous as the band turns up.

The place has a proper jazz feel. Minimalist interior. Buttoned down space. Refined acoustics. Pete takes advantage of the opening warm-up number to strut the jazz. He does the usual Herbie. Cantaloupe. Slips into a groove on the guitar, following Cyrus's shuffles in perfect time. The keyboard and sax chime in on cue. The audience is getting sucked into the jazz riffs. The band is on the money. Earning their keep. Then the lead singer muscles in.

Pete feels all refinement crushed as he's forced into 'Temple of Love'—that bastard Motown crap that audiences nevertheless seem to love. From the stage, he's horrified to see jazz sophisticates at La Boite cheering as the band replicates a twelve piece horn section with only an alto sax and a trombone to go around. Normally, the band do Temple of Love as an encore but the lead singer has decided it goes at the beginning—to 'mix it up a bit'. Pete notices that Flimsy's still wearing her GO BARCA! tee-shirt as she belts into the chorus. He suspects it's all going downhill from here.

I wake up with the sensation of a tightening in my groin. Look under the bedsheets and realise it's not the usual early morning onset of testosterone. My left testicle has swelled to the size of a grapefruit. Feel like the Buster Gonad character in Viz as I head gingerly towards the bathroom.

Luckily, I've pulled rank and booked my own room, ignoring Protesting Pete's pathetic whining about the unfairness, so I'm able to explore myself in private. I sit down on the bidet and delicately feel my way around the offending protuberance, trying to dampen down the escalating panic as snippets of vaguely digested information stampede into my head.

I recall reading about testicular torsion—where the arteries wrap around themselves and cut off the blood supply and your testicle ends up black and shrivelled and drops off like a withered vine. I poke it. It's painful, but it's not black.

I convince myself it's the result of too much Sangria. It'll get back to normal soon. I need to go onstage tonight. Sala Bikini. Big venue. There's a lot at stake. The telecoms company have spent a lot of money on publicity. They've plastered posters all over Barcelona. They're selling tickets at FNAC—the biggest music promoters in Spain. We've got adverts in the newspaper. We've got radio jingles. We can't afford to cancel the gig. The show must go on.

I remember what an Italian ex-girlfriend said to me when I skied into a tree in the Dolomites and broke my nose. In a health situation in southern Europe, milk your connections. I call up a bloke I've been working with who's a professor in the medical school at the Hospital del Mer. After a few cursory platitudes, he tells me to turn up at A&E.

I get a taxi and arrive at the entrance, where his minions are waiting. I'm escorted down a long corridor lined with punters in various stages of distress. They look up as the entourage sweeps regally past and I clock envy in their eyes. I get a full-on sneer from a particularly lairy-looking honcho who's pressing a gore-drenched handkerchief to a wound in his forehead. Looks for all the world like he's been ice-picked. Rock and Roll, mate, I sneer back.

Two hours of questions, probings, undignified examinations and painful blood tests follow. Doctors Garcia and Martínez are polite, professional and extremely conscious of their boss peering over their shoulders from his palatial office in the Faculty of Medicine two miles to the east.

They eventually come to a unanimous conclusion. Orchitis. Inflammation of the testicle. Probably bacterial. Typically associated with sexually transmitted infections like chlamydia. But the STI tests they've carried out, coupled with the fact that my recent sexual activity is comparable to that of an octogenarian Tibetan monk on Prozac, suggest that the origin of the orchitis is a bit of mystery.

We settle on a congenital bladder deformity as probable cause. I have history of congenital bladder deformity. It means that urine tends to accumulate in my bladder. With no means of escape, it gets more and more concentrated and ends up creating what amounts to a tropical holiday camp for bacteria.

The doctors give me an intra-muscular shot of ceftriaxone and a week's supply of doxycycline, plus a pack of naproxen to reduce the inflammation. They recommend I apply an ice pack to the offending gonad to further reduce the swelling. I thank them profusely and make a move towards the jacket that contains the pocket that accommodates my wallet. We all know it's a polite but unnecessary gesture. "Please," exclaim the doctors, "there is no charge. It's our pleasure."

"Muchas gracias," I reply. Two miles to the east, their boss is smiling.

Back at the hotel, I pillage the refrigerator for ice cubes, pack them in the plastic liner plucked from the toilet bin and insert it down my underwear. There's a sensation of instant relief. Hobble downstairs to the lobby where the band are expectantly assembled. It's an uncomfortable ride—particularly the initial cobble-stoned section before we get to the Diagonal and on to Sala Bikini.

We're the headline act, supported by a band that's a household name in Catalonia. As we pull up to the venue I notice a queue forming around its

160

perimeter—including a sub-queue that looks to be entirely composed of young women.

"Fucking hell," exclaims Duff, "we've got groupies."

He's right and wrong. There are groupies. But it turns out they're the other band's groupies. We're led into Sala Bikini by a woman in an impeccably cut black trouser suit. She shows us to our dressing room. It's a genuine Dressing Room. It has a room. And a dressing table. And Mirrors. And showers. Almost as good as the Mean Fiddler.

But topping the Fiddler there's an ice box the size of the Ritz. It's one of those coffin-shaped rectangular things with a glass top so you can see what's inside. And inside on a carpet of glistening ice cubes alcoholic goodies prostrate themselves before us. There's a slew of San Miguel. A nest of Jack Daniels. Pete lifts the lid reverentially. Hands dive in. I hoover a scoop of ice to replenish the testicular poultice.

With hindsight, it's obvious it was a big mistake to go on after the local band. First, because about ninety-nine per cent of the crowd had turned up to see them and not us. And second, because, in the intervening period between them and us, the contents of the ice-box had virtually disappeared. The promoter's contract had us on top of the bill, with the legendary local band up first. The logic of this was that the Catalan band would hook in all the punters, who'd then be primed and ready to worship at our altar when we came on after them. The first part of the logic worked like a dream.

By the time the Catalans came on stage, Sala Bikini was as packed as Ikea on a bank holiday weekend. They emerged to the kind of roar Barcelona get at a home game at Nou Camp. That's when I started to get the uneasy feeling, somebody hadn't done their homework in the promotional department.

The band look the exact opposite of us. They're wearing leather jackets and distressed jeans. The lead singer resembles an Albanian cage-fighter. They're all men. As the opening chords of what will inevitably turn into a Krautrock ear-shredder blast out, I turn to my band in supplication. They're displaying tell-tale signs of advancing inebriation.

By the time the Catalan band finish their set after seven increasingly frenetic encores half my band are so pissed they can barely pick up their instruments. We wander on stage or, in my case, dawdle. If anything, my enlarged testicle has got bigger. I'm struggling to perform even the pared back movements I normally do on stage. It's never been Mick Jagger, more like Marc Almond. But in this state,

I can't even raise a hop. The band think it's deliberate like I've been working on my stage presentation to look more cool.

"Any more chilled," says Pete as I shuffle around the stage during the warm-up, "and we'd be backing a corpse."

I take up my place alongside Flimsy. She's still wearing that fucking tee-shirt. Flimsy notices the bulge. "Been stuffing toilet rolls down your trousers again?"

I look down at the ice pack and realise it's diminishing. A small patch of damp is beginning to appear at the edges of my groin. I spend the rest of the set covering it with my hands, hoping the audience think it's part of my stage act.

I needn't have bothered. The Catalan band have stayed for our set, hanging around stage-side. They'd be drinking a well-earned cold San Miguel if there were any left in the ice-box. I'd spent the best part of the previous week planning the set-list. Meticulously choreographing the sequencing of the songs to take the audience on a journey they'd remember.

The plan was to get them relaxed with the opening instrumental. Then Flimsy and I go on stage and warm them up with the Holy Trinity—'Dirty Linen', 'Fire on Ice' and 'Victimised'. The Holy Trinity gets the Big Dipper going. As we progress through the set, each song ups the tempo. The Big Dipper gets faster and faster, pushed along by the thumping reggae bass-line of 'Words and Intentions' and the ridiculously cascading arpeggios of 'Ordinary Madness', before screaming to an explosive halt with 'Come to My Rescue'.

We give the audience time to recover in the interval before re-cranking the Big Dipper, finishing the set with 'Desperate, Lonely, Suicidal'.

'Dirty Linen' is a moody, broody emotion-mangler, its lyrics crafted to evoke loss, regret, retribution—"tang of sweat on the bedclothes/smear of perfume on the pillow/stab of moonlight at the window/Smokey playing on the radio." It starts off with a Latin feel—think Sade in 'Smooth Operator'—then accelerates to a relentlessly pounding middle eight as the song gets you in its grip, before re-enfolding you in its Latin embrace at the end.

Normally, it gets the audience's attention. But not in Sala Bikini. As I get to the end of the song, the point when the band stops playing and creates a space for my final, poignant last line—"never really knew you"—I can hear the chink of wine-glasses drowning out my vocals.

As we get into 'Fire on Ice'—a neat inversion of my current testicular predicament—it's hard not to notice the stream of punters heading for the exit.

162

It begins to dawn on me that my carefully-crafted set is wasted on this audience. They'd been given an hour of head-banging mayhem as a starter, then served nouvelle cuisine for the main course.

I needed to fight fire with fire. We'd have to radically re-jig the set list. Bring on the heavy hitters. I do a rapid tour around the band, whispering the new instructions. But by the time Pete cranks out the opening bars of 'Desperate, Lonely Suicidal'—a song that would surely appeal to even the Krautest of Krautrockers—it's too late. The Catalan band have disappeared, along with most of the audience.

The following day I'm summoned to a meeting with the man from the telecoms company. He's not very pleased. He takes a piece of paper from his briefcase and reads out a list of transgressions. I'm ticking them off in my head as he speaks. Appearance of intoxication on stage. Check. Failure to retain interest of audience. Check. Failure to retain interest of support act. Check.

I'm tempted to respond with a shrug and a 'Rock and Roll, mate' but what he says next renders me speechless. It appears that, despite all the money the company have invested in publicity, advance ticket sales for the Big One have been very poor. This, combined with our below-par performance at Sala Bikini, has led the company to decide regretfully to pull the plug. Bye bye publicity. Hasta la vista sponsorship. Finito Benito Big One.

The Big One. The tour's end. Its pinnacle. An appearance at Luz de Gas. Legendary Barcelona venue, with a history going back to the 1940s. It started as a cinema, re-invented itself as a theatre, reverted to a cinema and then turned into a cabaret club before making its name as concert hall.

There's plenty of Luz de Gas alumni to make you wonder how the fuck you got the gig. Eric Burdon and the Animals, Kool and the Gang, Canned Heat, ELO, John Cale, Bill Wyman, Simple Minds, the Corrs, Level 42—they all played Luz de Gas. The answer to the question of how I managed to get the gig is simple—I shamelessly played the HIV card and blagged powerful sponsors.

But now the powerful sponsors have pulled out. I make my way back to the hotel to give the band the bad news. I expected them to be upset at first, then to take it stoically—another set-back on the long and rocky road to stardom. But I got the opposite reaction. It was Pete—our resident bolshie—who, predictably, started it.

After I'd told them about the meeting with telecoms man, I suggested we use the three days left before we were due to fly back home to get some down-time.

Do some shopping. Take a walk round Gaudi Park. Visit the Picasso museum. Go to the beach at Barceloneta. I could see most of the band nodding in agreement. But not Pete. He's puffing his chest out like one of those uber-pigeons you see terrorising other pigeons in the park.

"Beach?" he spits, stabbing a claw in my direction. "It's fucking November." He's about to continue with a classic Pete diatribe but suddenly pauses. He's having a light bulb moment. You can almost see it glowing through his eyes.

"So, is the gig cancelled then?" he asks me.

I shrug. "Well, I guess so. The sponsors. They've all pulled out."

"Yeah, but is it cancelled, like actually?" He puts the stress on 'actually' as if accenting a particularly ponderous chord.

"Well, it's not officially cancelled as such," I reply, almost stuttering, like Cyrus, "but we've got no back-up, no publicity. We can't do the gig without back-up."

"Yeah," says Pete "but we've got these," and with a theatrical flourish he pulls a fat wedge of FNAC tickets from his guitar case and waves them in my face.

"Well then—let's do the show right here!" I sardonically reply, anticipating a laugh from the rest of the band.

But they're all looking expectantly at Pete. I'm feeling that familiar sensation of losing the dressing room.

"But who's going to buy tickets to see a band no-body outside London has heard of?" asks Flimsy.

"No-one's going to buy them," says Pete, a glint of triumph re-illuminating his face "We'll give them away for free."

We spend the next two days flying around the city, waylaying citizens at Metro stations. Hustling bar owners and shopkeepers. Smooth-talking tourists at the Gaudi cathedral. We plaster every bus-stop and hoarding along the Rambla with posters. We hand out copies of 'Desperate, Lonely, Suicidal?' to baffled football fans outside Nou Camp. We blag our way into the local radio station and get them to give us a plug.

By the time gig-zero dawns, the band is quietly confident. Three thousand tickets shifted. Hundreds of punters pledging their attendance. A big wave of interest was generated. Tonight we'll be surfing it.

Because it's a high-profile gig, we aim to get there in good time for the sound check. But it's a slow crawl from the hotel to the venue through the rush hour.

Max keeps losing his way in the city's gridiron side streets and by the time the van finally pitches up at the destination we're already half an hour late. I make out the shapes of masts and sails against a darkening sky. We're at the port. And there snugly tied up against the quayside is Luz de Gas.

We've never done a gig on a boat before. The band are looking perplexed as they extract the gear from the van and move it towards the venue. They're used to sweatily humping equipment up and down steep flights of steps in basement dives, not taking it for a leisurely stroll up a gangway. But the band is not as perplexed as the figure who greets us from a cabin doorway. The immaculate black dinner jacket and starched white shirt he's wearing combine with frenetic hand flapping to give the impression of a distressed seal.

"Senors," he says, the hand flapping intensifying, "¿Quién eres tú? Qué estás haciendo aquí?"

"We're the band, mate," replies Pete. "We need to do the sound check. Quick."

By now there's a pile-up in the doorway, its opening firmly blocked by the distressed seal's bulk. We're each trying to peer over the other's shoulder to get an eyeful of the interior. Ducking below Duff's armpit I manage to sneak a look inside. I make out tables in regimented rows, each covered by a crisp linen cloth on which cutlery, wine glasses and napkins are carefully arranged. I look upward and catch the seal's eye. "Where's the stage?"

"Stage?" he says, looking puzzled before a flash of recognition appears in his sealy eye and he lets out a bark of laughter.

"No hay escenario, Senor. Este es un restaurante. Restaurante Luz de Gas." He slips seamlessly into English.

"This is the Luz de Gas Restaurant. You want Luz de Gas club. It's on Muntaner. About twenty minutes from here."

Fuck. Schoolboy error. This is what happens when you let The Manager go and take on all the burro work yourself. We pile back into the van and head out to Diagonal, as I try to navigate with the aid of the hotel's tourist map and a wonky interior light. The ride is like snakes and ladders. We hare up a one way street, take the wrong turn and slide down another.

Finally, we get to the right Luz de Gas. In my head, I recall a plaque at the entrance listing the names of all the big-name acts that had performed there, including U2. But it must have been the stress. U2 have never played Luz de Gas—unless you count the tribute band—Banda Oficial U2. And there isn't a plaque. We hump the gear through the entrance and take in Luz de Gas. It's retained something of its cabaret roots by decking itself out as an old-style concert hall that looks a bit like the London Palladium with all the seats removed.

There's a gigantic main stage with huge velvet curtains, flanked by side stages topped by elaborate rococo plaster friezes depicting classical reclining figures in various stages of undress. At its centre, separated from the main stage by a wooden dance floor, is a gleaming bar the size of a cruise ship. To each side are satellite bars, like tug boats, their interiors illuminated by tiers of meticulously stacked bottles of spirits, twinkling like navigation lights. The whole place screams Lamborghinis and dirty banknotes.

The proprietor greets us like old friends. "It's a great honour to contribute to the fight against AIDS," he says as he steers the band towards the cavernous stage.

We do the sound check. Effortlessly supported by the three sound engineers up in their state-of-the-art engine room, we get a perfect mix. Ready to go. The Big One. I visualise myself in the imminent future, handing over a plump cheque to a smarmy salesman in the Bentley showroom.

It's still early, I tell myself as a solitary punter wanders into a space the size of Gaudi's cathedral, discovers he's on his own and wanders back out again. I send the nephew on. Sitting on a stool in the centre of the vast stage, framed by its waterfall of velvet curtains and clutching a twelve-string Yamaha he looks lost, a dot on the horizon. He opens with the acoustic version of 'Come as You Are'. Cobain's haunting melodics swirl around the empty concert hall.

A middle-aged couple drifts in and tip-toe to the shelter of one of the bars as if they've arrived late for the church service. The nephew ups the tempo and eases into Stevie Wonder's *Very Superstitious*. You have to hand it to him. It's eclectic—but inventive. And on he goes.

Ten iconic covers, each one signed, sealed and delivered with his own personal stamp. Pitch perfect. Shame there's no audience. The nephew finishes his set to a smattering of applause from the bar staff. He bows bashfully picks up his acoustic and disappears into the curtains. The proprietor turns to me and shrugs. "Senor," he says, "? Por Que."

I shrug back.

"Perhaps it's the weather," he says. I nod my head in agreement. The band is tantalisingly close to treading the same boards as John Cale, but I decide to call it a day. The bar staff outnumber the audience by a factor of ten. The shame potential is too great. We shake on it, the proprietor and me, as we bring it to a halt. The proprietor calls for drinks all round, including the bar staff. We drink a toast to the eradication of HIV.

We end up in Pipa, a legendary jazz club at the corner of Placa Real, perched above the Glacier Bar and sandwiched between a holiday flat letting company and a backpackers hostel. Invitation only unless you fork out a few euros for an instant membership card. It's like a miniature version of Luz de Gas, but there's more people.

50's decor. Faded leather upholstered settees. Wooden panelling. Art Deco lampshades. Old mahogany desks. Trophy cabinets filled with vintage saxophones and photographs of unrecognisable jazz dudes. Glass cases displaying smoking pipes. It's an open house at the bar. I get the impression word has spread and they're compensating us for the Luz de Gas debacle as if we are their own and we've been wounded and need looking after.

We take full advantage. Cyrus has always been partial to a malt whisky. Three hours later and we're navigating him down the narrow spiral staircase. Porno Dave takes his left arm. I've got his right. Brendan is holding on grimly to the left leg and the nephew is labouring under the strain of the other one. We manage to get him to the Glacier Bar and dump him in a taxi. The nephew volunteers to accompany him to the hotel. We retire to the Glacier Bar.

The morning after we arrive at El Prat after a fraught half-hour searching for gas stations in order to comply with the rental company's full-to-full fuel policy. The band dribble out of the van, falling onto the pavement outside the departure hall like a clutch of bedraggled chickens. They stand there each looking to various points of the compass for guidance. I do a personnel check. Amazingly, everyone is accounted for. Even the nephew. Flimsy's still wearing her tee-shirt. Some of the lettering has dropped off. It now reads 'GO B'.

We pass through security without incident, arrive at the departure gate. The band greets the Dan-Air 727 parked on the apron like we're being airlifted out of Saigon in the last days of the occupation. We run into turbulence as we head out over the water—the plane bumping and dipping as if shaken in the jaws of a giant cloud goblin. Cyrus quietly throws up into a sick-bag.

A band is what you start when you've finished with the ashram and the yoga. As I munched into the soft shell crab in the Que Viet the band came out of nowhere. It just popped into my head.

In retrospect, it ticked all the boxes. Re-colonise the territory your father annexed when he plucked you out of Liverpool School of Music and dropped you down in woolly-back land. Check. Opportunity to beat your father in the music success stakes. Check. Fast track to fame and riches without having to graft too much on the way. Check. Short circuit the tribal cycle of procrastination and putting up with things. Check check. Grab hold of the Beatles' legacy and add your light to the sum of Scouse musical lights. Check check check.

I'm having a night terror. I'm in the house in Liverpool. I'm seventeen or eighteen years old. I'm the oldest kid in the house. My siblings are running around the kitchen shouting and screaming. Their faces are the faces of my future children. My dad walks into the kitchen. He's just back from the boozer and his cheeks are flushed. He's wearing the frustrated expression of a man who's missed out on an argument. His fists are still clenched. He walks up to me and his face leans into mine, pent-up rage mixed with toxic Scotch whiskey.

How many plates have you used today?

I look blank.

There was a big pile of plates in the sink. Everyone else has only used one plate. And they've all been washed. Except yours. How many plates have you used today?

He smirks and meanders unsteadily down the hall. I pick up a plate from the pile in the sink and go to throw it, discus-style, as he turns to face me, still smirking. But the mass of the plate has dramatically multiplied. It's too heavy. I can't lift it. I can't throw it.

He smirks again and walks back through the kitchen to the cutlery drawer. Opens it. Takes out a breadknife. Comes up close. And, very deliberately, he slow-stabs the breadknife at my heart. I grab his hands and there's a strange mis-beat as I realise for the first time I am stronger. I turn his hands and the knife around and slowly and deliberately push it towards his chest. The knife turns to rubber. It bends pathetically. A joke knife. A schoolboy knife. A Lucky-Bag knife.

I'm labouring up the Pentonville Road in second gear, the Chinese-made pig-iron boneshaker I'd acquired from a car boot sale in Brick Lane sapping all my energy. An accumulation of lactic acid brings on the first spasm of cramps in my calves.

In the last hundred metres before the traffic lights at Upper Street, I'm passed by a pensioner on a Brompton fold-away, the slipstream buffeting my cheeks as it glides effortlessly away, breasting the rise at the Tube station before zipping down towards Old Street. I'm engulfed by anger. An invisible elastic band now tethers me to the Brompton. It's imperative I catch it up. I begin reeling in the distance.

Then I realise I've left Janine behind. Slam the brakes on. The pig-iron screeches and grinds to a halt. I pull in and wait for her to catch up. When she reaches me, she clocks my sweaty red-faced rage. She looks at me as if I'm the Tomato from Outer Space. What are you like, she says. One minute we're pottering around on our bikes. The next you're off like a lurcher after a rabbit. Chasing some poor old dear on her way to get her hair done. What is it with you? You have to compete with everyone. Everything. All of the time.

Even yoga. As I'm in the inverted triangle of downward dog I peer furtively at my fellow yogis to check if anyone's doing it better than me. I'm a prisoner of family, tribe and neurosis. It seems I'm a prisoner of cultural memory too. Human neurology retains and re-configures the cultural equivalent of the genetic code, the architectural blueprint for constructing survival machines. The psychologist Paul McLean was the first to recognise that 'emotions' are hard-wired in the brain.

A decade later, the Soviet neuropsychologist, A R Luria showed that the evolution of the brain was shaped by culture: "It is a complex of functional systems, organised according to plans and programmes created by man's social history."

In 1974, Donald Campbell coined the term 'evolutionary epistemology' to describe the how knowledge itself evolves through natural selection. In 1981, Lumsden and Wilson argued that genetic evolution and cultural evolution work together. They suggested that 'culture' was composed of physical units made of networks of neurons in the brain. These units function as 'memory'. Towards the end of 'The Selfish Gene', Dawkins put forward the idea that a new kind of replicator had recently emerged. He called it the 'meme'.

Dawkins said that humans are unique as a form of 'survival machine' for genetic success. What separates humans from other survival machines is culture. The history of human civilisation is a narrative of a particular form of evolution. Different civilisations emerge. They create particular forms of cultural artefacts—houses; temples; jewellery; pottery. They come to dominate the cultural practices of a particular era; they decline and then sometimes they die.

As Susan Blackmore said what makes humans different from other species is the capacity to imitate. Humans can pass on ideas from one person to another. All these ideas are memes—and memes, like genes, are replicators.

Humans are the slaves of memes. Memes are now driving genes. They have become the dominant replicator. Our 'self' was created by and for the memes. We have no free will and our consciousness is not the driving force of our behaviour. We are meme machines through and through.

Memes built the pyramids. They were responsible for forcing nomadic but contented, hunter-gatherers into the unending toil of farming, with its attendant crop failures and starvation. They invented God. They created witches and ducking stools. They persuaded rational beings to wear lederhosen. They precipitated the Wall Street Crash. They herded people into lap dancing clubs. And they came up with Donny Osmond.

I invented the band to escape The Stuckness. I thought it would extricate me from the straight-jacket of family, church and school. I used the band to eradicate the memory of those sweaty clutches with Father O'Dirty. I weaponised the band to counter-punch my father. I employed it to deflect the emotional pain of build-ups, let-downs, break-ups and illusory start-ups.

As I delved into my ancestry, it seemed clear that in my head lay some long-buried collective memories of the boglands through which my tribal ancestors—the Reivers—marauded. And the band could somehow offer me a safe passage from those boglands. But it seems I'm just replicating Donny Osmond.

I get a call from my Mother. She sounds distressed. Then she tells me the bad news. My dad had gone to the pub for Quiz Night. As usual, she hadn't waited up for him and had gone to bed. But when it had got to midnight and he hadn't arrived home, she began to worry.

She got dressed and went down to the pub. It was locked shut. She rang the bell but got no answer. She went back home and just as she arrived the phone rang. It was the local hospital. My dad had collapsed on the way back from the pub, in the alleyway that connects the main road with the housing estate. Some neighbours had found him as they walked home. He's had a stroke.

December

The hangover from the Barcelona tour lasted longer than I expected. We re-group at the rehearsal studio for the next gig. The band are tired, sullen, bored, spent. They've put in enough spade work this past year to expect a decent return on investment and they're wondering why the recording contract fairy hasn't paid them a visit.

Pete isn't backwards in coming forward with the blame. "If you hadn't given The Manager the elbow," he says, "the tour would've been better organised. And we'd have a bigger profile."

Cyrus and Flimsy are nodding in support. On any other day, I'd have pushed back and precipitated the inevitable row. So the band looks slightly mystified when I make a conciliatory response. "You're right, Pete," I say. "Hands up. It was a poor show on my part," and I hold my hands up to emphasise the point.

They're not sure if I'm taking the piss, but it's enough to stem the grumbling. "Let's move on. Per ardua ad astra. Onwards and upwards. The more we practice the better we get. The better we get, the more we get noticed," and I dish out the set list for the next gig. They're clearly not convinced but set up anyway and after a few half-tantrums with equipment, we begin to get into rehearsal groove.

But I'm being disingenuous. For out of a clear blue sky, the recording contract fairy *has* paid us a visit. The Manager—not being the vindictive type— had forwarded me the mail she'd received for the band. When we'd got back from Barcelona, there was a sheaf of it waiting for me on the doormat. I leafed through it. There was one envelope that bore the logo of Sony Music. I sliced it open expecting the usual supercilious kiss-off but, on speed-reading, it spread itself, lotus-like, to reveal mouth-watering promise. It's from one of their A&R representatives. It says:

Many thanks for sending your demo CD to us. I have listened to it and would like to see how the band looks and sounds in a live setting. Could you please send me a list of your planned performances in the next month, including venues and dates, together with a contact telephone number.

It ends with a real signature. Inked, not photocopied.

One of The Manager's last actions before we parted ways was to get us a gig at the Half Moon in Putney. Although technically it's a pub, the significance of the Half Moon in the music pantheon shouldn't be under-estimated. In the '60s, it hosted Ralph McTell, John Martyn, Bert Jansch, Roy Harper, John Mayall's Bluesbreakers, Alexis Korner, The Yardbirds and Fairport Convention. Van Morrison played there. So did The Who.

Over the years it added more A's to its list. Nick Cave turned up. Elvis Costello did a residency. Debut performances include k.d. lang's first UK appearance, Kate Bush's first ever public outing and U2's first UK gig. It also helped launch the career of a local band—the Rolling Stones. It's an auspicious planetary alignment.

Our upcoming gig at one of the most iconic music incubators on earth coinciding with an expression of interest from one of the biggest record producers on earth. I write back to the A&R man pronto, express delivery, inviting him to the Half Moon. Two days later I get a call from his PA confirming A&R man's attendance.

I waited until we'd finished the rehearsal before I dropped the fairy-bomb. We'd gone through the set-list for the Half Moon and the band were just finishing packing their gear away when I made the announcement. I'd delivered the usual speech reminding them of where we were playing and when we needed to turn up for the sound check.

"Oh and by the way," I said as they headed for the exit, "the A&R man from Sony is on the guest list."

It took a while to register. Flimsy didn't take it in at all. Max gave a nod of acknowledgement on his way to the door. Pete was halfway through the door when he turned and looked back at me.

"What the fuck are you saying?" he asks, looking incredulous. "Are you saying Sony Music is turning up?"

I nod smugly. "The very same. Their A&R guy is coming to the gig especially to see us."

Pete looks like he's torn between doing a jig and smacking me in the head. "Why the fuck didn't you tell us before?"

172

It's an interesting question. Call me a card-carrying control freak. Call me a paternalistic narcissist who likes to dispense gifts to his offspring. Call me a sadistic bastard who likes to see his minions squirm. All these things are true. "I wanted it to be a surprise," I say. "Now let's turn up at the Half Moon on Saturday and kill them stone dead. No prisoners."

If this was meant to be a speech to rally the troops, it wasn't having its intended effect. They look like they're shitting themselves.

Saturday comes. D-Day. Drum fight at the Sony Corral. I'd given the band a pep-talk before we left for the sound-check, reminding them of all the legends who'd preceded us. Big Mistake. As I did the roll call of all the A-listers who'd played the Half Moon I could see the weight on their collective shoulders grow bigger. In the end, I resorted to the all-time classic cliché "Just do your best."

It started auspiciously. Soundcheck—pass. Assemble equipment on stage efficiently and effectively—check. Sizeable audience gathering expectantly— tick. We kick off with the usual instrumental warm-up. Cantaloupe. The band flexing its muscles, getting into a groove. Me and Flimsy appear on cue as Cantaloupe winds down. Thank God she's not wearing her GO BARCA! tee shirt. Instead, she's wearing the feather boa.

Learning from the Barcelona debacle, I've taken the decision to stick with the meticulously choreographed set-list we'd started with Bikini, on account of the Half Moon not having a bunch of Krautrock head-bangers on the undercard to fuck it up. So, Flimsy and I warm them up with the Holy Trinity—'Dirty Linen', 'Fire on Ice' and 'Victimised'.

We up the tempo with 'Words and Intentions', then take them into the townships with 'Ordinary Madness' before slipping effortlessly into 'Come to My Rescue'—the ridiculously baroque mini-opera I'd concocted from chitterlings of Figaro and Bohemian Rhapsody. Flimsy's putting her soul into it and giving it her best Essex diva in the duet. I swear I can see a few tears shed in the audience as she warbles out "I'm not a cure you can take down from the medicine shelf."

But tears are not what I'm scanning for. I'm looking for him. Mr A&R. King Sony. I wouldn't know him from a cucumber but such is my desperate need to wish him here, in the flesh, in the crowd, that I'm convinced I'll know who he is as soon as I set eyes on him.

The interval gives the audience a chance to rein in their emotions. We kick off the second half of the set with 'Hope Street'. I'd had to argue the toss at rehearsal to get the band to agree to include it in the set at all. Half of them—and you know who they are, don't you—saw it as a risky choice. The lyrics contain a few phrases that could be described as industrial and they didn't want the band to appear too unwholesome under the unforgiving glare of the Great Eye of Sony.

I'd categorise Hope Street as one of my 'Dickens' songs—over-the-top diatribes that feature social injustice. I'd got the idea from a Liverpool street of the same name. I'd been walking through Toxteth on one of my rare visits back to my roots to see some family and I'd been struck by the number of hookers, dealers and junkies on the streets.

There was a particular girl I noticed. She looked really young from a distance, but when I got closer, she looked much older. As I came level with her I could see the track marks on her arms. She leaned into me as I was passing her, "Do you want any business?"

Anyone familiar with Liverpool knows that Hope Street—though it backs onto Toxteth—is actually an elegant, up-market area located in what's known as the Canning Georgian Quarter, flanked by the two cathedrals and commonly regarded as one of the best streets in the city. But I couldn't resist the conceit of using it to make a Statement of Irony—the street of hope in name, the street of despair in reality. I also wanted to give religion a kicking by painting those great cathedrals as symbols of hypocrisy.

Some of the band don't like it from a musical perspective. I can see why. It's a bit of a departure from our jazz funk roots. More Pearl Jam than Level 42. Pared down. No frills. No sax. No piddly guitar riffs. Lots of distortion and fuzz. The drum kit is in the driving seat. 112 BPM. It begins with a four bar intro—straight grand piano, no effects—Gm7, sliding down the scale, the melody anchoring verse 1–8 bars, repeating Gm7 before dropping to Em5 and ending on D to dramatically change the tone:

She was standing there on Hope Street
nineteen going on thirty-five
she said for twenty you can fuck my face
to keep me alive.

Verse 2 drops to Em5–6 bars—ending on a more hopeful note in C major:

She's got a habit that's as deep as hell
her mission mapped in lines
all the stories she could tell
of a child of the times.

But C major lures the listener into a false sense of security. There's a four bar instrumental linking passage that repeats the E minor—C major riff, ending on D major, that pre-figures verse 3:

To the sound of the cathedral bell
while the pilgrims prayed for guidance from above
she showed me what she had to sell
and she said—this is all—the closest that you get to love.

The last line in verse 3 features a driving drum and bass riff that sucks you into the chorus—C, D and G major then C, D dropping to E minor:

And she say
take me to a higher plane
take me to a higher plane

There's an 8 bar guitar solo before verse 4, which repeats the musical structure of verse 3 and segues back into the chorus:

She don't care about your family values
She don't care about your little white books
She don't care about the temple and the tower
She don't care about your pedigree, she don't care about your looks
And she say
take me to a higher plane
take me to a higher plane

Then the 4 bar pared down piano intro is reprised and we repeat verse 1, ending with 4 repetitions of the chorus.

Contrary to my expectations, Flimsy loves it. Probably because she gets to belt out the chorus six times. Unfortunately, she keeps singing 'take me to a higher place' instead of 'plane'. I'm convinced this is a deliberate attempt to sabotage the song, rather than a manifestation of her lack of literacy. Hope Street is sombre, measured, atmospheric and melodic. The crowd love it too.

We finish the set with 'Desperate, Lonely, Suicidal?', followed by the obligatory 'Temple of Love'. It's a wrap. The crowd are on their feet. There's calls for an encore. We don't do encores. We don't have anything left in the repertoire. But we've delivered. I still don't know if all that effort has been wasted. I don't know if King Sony has even turned up. We're packing away the gear when I get a tap on the shoulder. It's the bar manager. He tells me there's someone who'd like to meet me. He's in the private room at the back of the pub.

I expected him to be young, brash and wearing chinos. So I'm not prepared for the pin-striped, late-career Travolta that stands up to greet me as I enter the room. He gestures me to take a seat opposite. Hands me a neat Scotch. Fixes me with the kind of high-interest-rate smile you get when you ask your bank manager for an overdraft.

"So you're the organ-grinder in this outfit," he says extracting a handful of peanuts from a bowl placed in the centre of the table. He offers me the bowl.

"No thanks," I say. "I read in the paper that over ninety per cent of pub peanuts have traces of urine on them."

The smile goes down a few notches as he deposits the remnants of his peanuts back in the bowl. He takes a sip of scotch and leans back in his chair.

"You've obviously been around the block a few times," he says. "Doing the circuits. Clocking up the gigs. Going round and round the merry-go-round. To be honest, you're a bit long in the tooth. Normally, we're looking for fresh meat. Bands we can punt out to the young people, with their grand delusions of immortality and quirkiness. Bands they can identify with."

I give a shrug. The fact that he's turned up, stayed for our set and is still here, talking to me, tells me there must be some profit angle he's considering.

"Well, we are what we are. I won't pretend we're the next Bay City Rollers. But we're a tight band. We've got good musicians. The material's interesting. It's different. Remember Bohemian Rhapsody? No-one ever thought that would be one of the biggest selling singles of all time."

He lets out a chuckle that could best be described as restrained. "I think we'd both agree that I'm not having a conversation with the lead singer of the next Queen."

"Maybe not, but I'd say we've got something that might be of interest, otherwise we wouldn't be having the conversation."

He gives a slight nod that could be construed as an acknowledgement. "It's possible we could package something, do some market shaping, pitch you at thirty-somethings with disposable income." He takes another sip of scotch and adjusts his shirt cuffs so they emerge at the appropriate angle.

"I quite like your stuff," he says. "Needs a bit of polishing. The vocals could do with beefing up. We need to take the pruning shears to some of the material. Like that song about the hooker who gets taken to a higher place. But on the whole, it's a foundation we could build on."

He takes another sip of scotch. "We don't sign bands straight off. I'll tell you what I'll do. I'll give you six months in the studio. You'll work with our people—engineers, music coaches and so forth. And if we see something we can use at the end of it, we'll give you a contract. How's that sound?"

It sounds fucking-A to me. I'm repressing a desire to rear up from my seat, grab him by the lapels and smother him with hot kisses. I restrain myself, try to look nonchalant. "I think it's something we could work with," I say, necking the last dregs of the scotch.

"I'll get my PA to send you the details," he says. He gets up and picks up his briefcase. "To the future," he says, offering me his hand.

I take and shake it. "Thanks for the opportunity. I'm sure you won't be disappointed," I say.

He bows slightly and turns towards the exit. "Oh and don't forget," I call as he's halfway through the door, "Lay off the peanuts."

I emerge from my Interview with the Vampire to be immediately encircled by the band. They can hardly contain themselves.

"What did he say?" I can't help grinning.

"Top result," I tell them. "They're giving us six months free studio time with an option to sign us up if things go well."

I'm not sure what I expected in response. Optimistic scenario—I'm engulfed in a scrum of grateful bandmates, all slapping me on the back. Pessimistic scenario—they're nodding in recognition of my significant achievement but still thinking about all the work we need to put in to take advantage of the opportunity we've been given. What I hadn't factored into the equation was their sense of entitlement—as if putting in the hours on the treadmill had guaranteed them a berth in the rock and roll trough.

As ever, it's Pete who kicks off the confrontation. "What do you mean?" he says. "Six months in the studio? We could work our bollocks off for free and get nothing at the end of it."

"That's true," I respond, "but we've been working our bollocks off for two years for less than free. We still owe money for the CD. We've never made a penny out of all the gigs we've done. Don't you realise who's just offered us a deal? It's Sony Music—as in Sony Music, Madison Avenue, New York City. As in Bob Dylan, Aretha Franklin, Whitney Houston, Michael Jackson, Bruce Springsteen, AC/DC, Leonard Cohen."

"But it's not a fucking deal," says Pete. "It's worth fuck all. It's not a contract. It's a pile of shite. We could spend the next six months in their studio. All the time not knowing if what we do will amount to anything. All the time not knowing if they'll just give us the elbow at the end of it."

I turn to the band. "Let's discuss it. Everyone can have their say and when we've finished discussing it, let's come to a decision."

Cyrus takes up the invitation, deploying God metaphors to articulate his position. The band is being forced into Purgatory—halfway between heaven and hell. We're at the mercy of an Omnipotent who's final judgement is unknown and unpredictable. Better to cut our losses and cut Sony adrift, go back to gigging and look for better opportunities.

Flimsy takes her cue, looking even angrier than when I instructed the sound engineer to turn down her volume at the Rock Garden. "It's a joke," she says. "They're taking the piss. I bet they do this to all the bands they come up with. Stick them in a studio and then wave them bye-bye at the end of it. We deserve better. They should be giving us a contract."

I'm tempted to point out the inconsistencies in her logic, like the studio offer is in fact a contract, but feel sandbagged by her spleen. I look to the others for support. Max is projecting discomfort, shifting his weight from one foot to the other.

"Well, it's not what I'd hoped for," he says. "It's a bit disappointing. It leaves us kind of in a no man's land. We do studio time and then what? It's not like they're giving us a recording contract. We might end up worse than we are now."

I look towards Brendan and Duff. They're sitting on the fence, as always. They both shrug. Whatever.

Pete seizes on their silence as an opportunity to pile in again. "And what about the copyright," he says, "if we create stuff in their studio, does it mean they own the material?"

Not being a music law specialist I'm on shaky ground here but I muster enough authority in my tone to appear as if I know what I'm talking about. "Of course not," I say confidently, "it'll be just like it is now. Whoever writes the song owns the song."

"So the band owns the material."

"Well, not really," I reply. "Most of the stuff we do on stage and the stuff that's on the CD is down to me. If you look at the sheet music for 'Ordinary Madness', where it says words and music, you'll see my name. If you look at Rok-beat, it's got Cyrus's name next to it."

Pete looks like he's about to spontaneously combust. "That's total bullshit," he screams. "Every song we do. All the creative stuff that goes into it. That comes from the band. You just come up with the ideas. You can't even read music. You couldn't tell an E flat from a pork chop."

"It's not just ideas, Pete," I respond. "I may not be able to read music that well. But I can write it. And where do you think all the lyrics come from? Name me one song this band has produced that hasn't come from me or now and again, from Cyrus."

"But these songs you write. They're just scribbles on the back of an envelope. It's the band that brings them to life. So, they should be credited to the band."

As Pete foams on I'm doing some quick mental arithmetic. It doesn't take long to work out that royalties divided by seven—where the band has an equal share—is a lot less than royalties divided by two, where I get the composition royalties and the recording royalties are split between the band. But not for the first time, Pete's soap-box oratory has roused the rabble. By the set of the band's faces, it's looking like I've got a mutiny on my hands. Time for some tact and diplomacy.

"We can work something out," I say placatingly. "Like if the music on a song's been substantially changed from my original, then the band can be credited with the music."

Pete's shaking his head. "No chance. We're all in this together," he says, sounding like a character from a Dumas novel.

"That's fine. It's easy to acknowledge the band's contribution. We can just put something like 'arranged by the band' on the CDs."

Pete looks incredulous. "Arranged by," he sneers. "You'll have to do better than that. More like 'blood sweat and tears shed by the band to turn this piece of shit into a proper song'."

I'm looking at him standing there, pigeon chest puffed out, hands on hips, like the Angry Kid in the playground. And I get the proverbial rush of blood to the head. All the effort I've put into the big dream—grovelling to dodgy club-owners; soothing egos; dealing with sound check shit storms; wondering whether anyone is going to turn up; wondering whether anything I've ever written is worth anything—it all clusters into one big toddler tantrum.

"Well, fuck you all," I shout. "This is the biggest thing that's ever happened to us—and what are you doing? You're shitting it. You don't have the bollocks to take it on. You don't have the fucking commitment. You basically just don't have what it takes."

I shouldn't have been surprised by the response. Predictably, it's Pete who reacts first. "Well, fuck you too," he snarls, slamming his guitar case into the studio wall. "I'm done with this shit. You go into the fucking Sony studio on your own and see what you come up with."

He storms out the door theatrically. Flimsy follows. "I'm done too," she flounces.

Cyrus is methodically packing up his gear. He issues comments at each stage. Stacks up the cymbals, "Bad deal." Disassembles the conga, "Deserve better." Puts the bass drum into its protective covering. "I'm out."

Max shuffles his feet and looks at the floor. "Sorry, boss," he says. "I'm with Cyrus and Flimsy on this."

The two greenhorns are too cowed to deliver much opposition. "Well," says Duff, "I think it's good they're giving us the studio. But I can see the point of what everyone else is saying."

Brendan nods. "I agree with Duff."

I'm thinking about counter-arguments to get them back on track. But I'm looking at them and I can see it would be futile. They don't want to make it. It's obvious. Die Band ist Kaputt. Fertig. "OK," I say to what's left of the band. "Looks like we're done. Let's call it a day. But we still owe money for the CD."

So here we are. They'd agreed to go ahead with our last booking on the calendar so we can pay off the remaining costs of the CD. Final gig of the year. Final gig of the band. Christmas Eve. Stoke Newington. The Samuel Beckett. Classic live music pub venue. Always gets a full house.

I remember going there to see Luddy Samms and the Deliverers. Luddy— ex-Drifters singer—cv as long as a giraffe's neck—stints with James Brown, Otis Redding and Stevie Windwood; one time club owner—Turnmills in Clerkenwell, the legendary Four Aces in Dalson and Luddy's Lounge in Kentish Town. He chalked up a clutch of legal disputes with former bands over name rights, including a long-standing litigation handbag with the Drifters.

Luddy came on stage at the Samuel Beckett to a packed house, wearing a silver lurex suit and milked it to within an inch of its life with a set of Motown show-stoppers, ending with a bravura tap-dance along the Beckett's bar-top to thunderous applause.

We assemble outside the venue. Everyone is avoiding each other's eyes. It's freezing so we hurry inside. The arctic air creeps in behind and saturates the bar. Insinuates itself inside the instruments. Brendan's E string snaps as he's tuning up. Cyrus's bass drum sounds muffled as if encased in a duvet. Flimsy is rubbing her hands and stamping up and down to generate heat. The barman takes pity and dispenses cheap brandies all round to warm us up.

The band lurches into the opener. Same old same old. Cantaloupe. Drums struggling for pace. Keyboard wheezing like a smoker. Me and Flimsy take our places for Words and Intentions and I'm scanning the room to check the audience.

But there is only a bean-hatted moaner wedged in a corner. Half asleep. Snorting like a brontosaurus. His Pitbull was chained to a table leg, licking its anus. It howls as we finish the chorus. We plough on through the set. I've got one eye on the entrance, half expecting a late surge of revellers to come bursting through, but as we finish with 'Temple of Love', we're still playing to bean-hat and his pit-bull.

Normally, we use the concluding bars of 'Temple of Love' to introduce the band to the audience. Ladies and Gentlemen, on bass guitar, the King of the Strings, Mr Brendan Bazzle. On rhythm guitar—coaxing the love from those worn-out frets—it's Pete Dankpatch. On drums—all the way from East Finchley, via the Cape of Good Hope—it's the Prince of the Hi-Hats, the Titan of Toms, the Sultan of Snare, Mr Cyrus Dactyl.

On horn, let's hear it for that sultry seducer of the saxophone, Mr Max Beauregard. Caressing the ivories, on keyboards, Mr Duff Jones. Belting out the backing vocals, please give it up for Miss Flimsy Wipers. And from me, thank you for listening. We love you all.

But there's only the bean-hatted moaner and his pit-bull. I pick up the mike. The band are still looping the final bars of Temple of Love around an endless circuit. I cut in.

"Ladies and Gentlemen, I'd like to introduce the audience to the band. On bean-hat, it's Mr Bean Hat. On scratch-board, it's Mr Scratchy-anus-pit bull. On pints and glasses, it's Mr Bar Staff. I'd like to wish everyone a Merry Christmas and a Happy New Year. Thank you for all your support and we'll see you on the twelfth of never."

Duff thinks it's a hoot and beams out a big cheesy grin. But Pete's giving me the evil eye and Cyrus is shaking his head, looking like a prim schoolmarm who's star pupil has just dropped a particularly ripe fart in the middle of a poetry recital. The band grinds to a halt. We vacate the stage, pack up the instruments. The barman gives Bean-hat a shake and he quivers into consciousness. Unchains the Pitbull. Heads for the exit.

I move over to the bar manager to initiate the financial transaction. He's not happy with the hundred quid he's having to fork out for an audience of two if you include the animal, but it's one of those gigs where we've agreed on a flat rate rather than bums on seats. You win some, you lose the majority.

We drag the gear outside. A thin styrofoam of snow has covered the pavement and the street is hushed, even though it's not yet midnight. Cyrus loads Max and his kit into the Mondeo. Brendan stows Duff's Yamaha in the boot of the still pristine BMW. Flimsy's motorcade glides up to the kerb and she's absorbed into the interior of a Subaru 4X4, like an East End Imelda Marcos. Pete mounts his bike and vanishes into a miniature flurry as if disappearing inside my Fatima igloo.

There they all go. No tears and no hearts breaking, no remorse. Leaving me, numero uno, lead singer, on a pavement in Stoke Newington, in a gently falling admonishment of snow, alone. It's the day after my birthday. I'm forty years old.

I decide to walk back to the house. The buses have stopped and the minicabs will be charging double rate for Christmas Eve. It's a long slow trek down the Kingsland Road. People are spilling out of the Rochester, which seems to have sucked in all the crowd we should have had in the Samuel Beckett. A woman wearing a crop top who's hanging on to a tall bloke in a Moss Bros dinner jacket staggers across my path.

"Merry Christmas," she slurs.

"And you," I mutter through gritted teeth. As I trudge on I'm replaying the Half Moon in my head, trying to work out why the band reacted to the golden goose as if it had laid a wet turd.

And then, as I'm navigating around a conga of carousers streaming out of the White Hart, the truth whacks me round the head like a sock full of billiard balls. It wasn't fear of failure that pushed the band's buttons—it was fear of success. A textbook case of Achievemephobia. They pretended to hate the treadmill of second-division gigs, the indignity of changing into stage gear in the toilets, the pain of enduring a barrage of drunken heckling and the ignominy of accepting pitiful gate money from a rapacious club-owner at the end of the night. But deep down, they were comfortable with it.

They don't actually want to change the situation because that situation signifies success on their own terms. A recording contract offers the possibility of success on someone else's terms, terms over which they have no control. Although it looks like they'd kicked off because they hadn't been given a recording contract straight off, it dawns on me it's just an excuse. So was the row over copyright.

What really happened was that Sony's offer of studio time had brought the mythical recording contract one step closer to reality. On the circuit, despite its pissed-up audiences and flying bottles, they'd operated in a gentle, forgiving half-light that had smoothed the missed beats, the bum notes, the off-key vocals. It sandpapered all the band's warts. But with Sony's offer, there was a possibility that at the end of studio time, they'd be pushed out into the unforgiving glare of big time—exposing all those warts. So what they did was sabotage the offer.

I reach the junction of Kingsland Road and Shacklewell Lane. Turn right and I'm home. The cat is waiting. I soothe him down and go upstairs, pour myself a king-sized measure of twelve-year-old Talisker. Go upstairs to the living room. Sit down on the settee. Slide the band's CD into the player and listen to what Sony will be missing out on. And as Flimsy's impassioned plea for understanding rings out in 'Come to My Rescue', I realise in a cattle prod instant of awakening that all that operatic artifice I'd created was self-indulgent wank. The maunderings of someone who hadn't gotten over being dumped.

Harry Hazell was right. It was all tinkly-tosh. Instead of penning crypto-Mozart duets, I'd have been better off listening to my inner punk and banging off three minute broadsides against global capitalism.

But—hold on there, dude—I already have a three minute broadside against global capitalism. It's called 'Desperate, Lonely Suicidal?'. The genesis of a plan begins to stir. 'Desperate', 'Hope Street' and a new song I'd almost finished called 'Burger-land'. The Unholy Trinity. Perfect combination for a new demo EP. Recorded by a new band and sent straight to my new mate at Sony. No twittering guitar arpeggios. No fussy horn solos. No tinny piano. No tinkly-tosh. Just pure grunge.

Names for the new band are already popping into my head. Pernicious Weeds. Free Radicals. It's all beginning to fall into place. Per ardua ad astra. Onwards and upwards. I eject the former band's demo and insert another CD into the player. Mozart's Requiem soars out through the speakers. I turn it up to full volume. Fuck the neighbours.

The ward is painted an eggshell that is meant to be neutral but which weeps quiet desolation. There's a broken window at one end. It has a sign attached that says 'Urgent Repair Required', though the date shown had expired two weeks before. Another window set in a side wall looks out onto a courtyard flanked by brown-brick buildings. I glimpse the branches of trees waving in the distance.

My father is in the third bed on the left. His neighbour, a very old, completely bald man, lies motionless, eyes closed, hands neatly arranged on the coverlet. His face has the pallor of white fish laid out too long. I approach my father. This was the bruiser who once knocked cold a man who had insulted him. The man had mistaken my father for an Italian.

This was the man who, with his taunts, had goaded me into punching the living room wall, causing me to break my little finger. This was the colossus who, at the epicentre of a mad crowd surge in a corridor at Old Trafford football stadium, had perched me on his shoulders and then had calmly beaten a path through the panic-stricken herd, as if scything weeds. Now he was a diminished thing as if a medical student had left a shrunken head on a pillow for a joke.

The bed is fitted with a device that periodically circulates a puff of compressed air through the mattress. It's like a dry water bed, undulating the mattress to save nurses from having to turn the occupant. It is meant to prevent bedsores and is calibrated according to the patient's weight. From the setting on the visual display, I could see that my father now weighed just over one hundred pounds, some fifty pounds less than in his prime as a welterweight.

In sleep, his face, despite the hospital pallor, looked almost cherubic—the eyelashes in particular long, lush and curved like those of an infant. My mother was at the bedside. She looked more exhausted even than my father—the legacy of a drawn-out nocturnal vigil. In spite of everything—the relentless abandonment; the episodic violence—even the finality of divorce—she was still there, looking after; bearing up.

The divorce had been a typical act of misplaced brinkmanship. The irony was that my father had initiated the divorce, mistaking my mother's provocative excursion into toy-boy territory as the real thing, rather than a cri de coeur. After the divorce, they still lived together in the same house. I wondered which of the three things driving her onward in this endless waltz—duty, guilt and love—was now dominant.

She looked up as I entered and gave me the smile that mothers reserve for the first born male, both welcoming and forgiving.

"He's sleeping," she said.

It was a superfluous observation, but it somehow stamped an imprimatur of authority on the situation—as if only her diagnosis could be believed in a world of white-coated charlatans. Confirming a lifetime of insubordination, my father chose this moment to wake up. He opened his eyes, looked at me and uttered the kind of salutation that had defined our serrated relationship over the years:

"All right, baldy?"

He seemed cheerful under the circumstances. It was difficult to decipher what he was saying, because of the ischaemic stroke that had transformed his voice from a velvet tenor to a dry croak. Yet the rich vein of mordant wit had not diminished. He was breathing in oxygen through two small tubes, one in each nostril. There were two drips inserted in his right arm—one for antibiotics and one for pumping out electrolytes to maintain fluid balance.

The left arm was horribly swollen and stamped with livid purple bruises— the result, I supposed, of the fall and subsequent pneumonia that had landed him in this place. I later found out that most of the swelling had been caused after staff had stripped him of his nightgown and shoe-horned him into pyjamas. He must have been in some pain, though he didn't show it and he didn't complain.

I asked a nurse for a vase for the flowers I had brought but was told that, for the comfort and safety of patients and staff, flowers were not allowed. I pulled up a plastic chair and set it near the head of the bed, so I could better catch what my father was saying.

We had never had what you might call a proper conversation, my father and I. The discourses we had shared over the years could be split into two kinds:

185

confrontations and accommodations. The confrontations usually sprang from divergent ideological positions. I remember one that took place in the small kitchen of my parent's house, on one of the rare occasions the family came together to mark some milestone or other, like a christening or a funeral.

Stepping into his shoes, I can see this cocky young, long-haired upstart, breezing in from the University course my father had subsidised, in a car he'd paid for, swigging lager from his fridge and pontificating about dialectical materialism.

"What we need is a revolution in this crap country," I would say, taking another lager from the refrigerator.

"What you need is to spend a few years in a ship's engine room," he would retort, "and then tell me about revolution."

Unable to match him physically, I used the education he'd never had to develop and hone my intellectual ringcraft, dazzling him with stinging combinations of verbal jabs and mental uppercuts. I followed this up with behaviour that was diametrically opposed to his values and beliefs. Just to piss him off, I used to drive the kind of car that would be guaranteed to send him into a snowstorm of head-shaking and tutting.

There were exotic rust buckets, like the Sunbeam Tiger, its twin Weber carburettors choking to a standstill after a few miles; its seat-wells slopping with dirty rainwater following the lightest of spring showers. There were superannuated chav-mobiles like the Ford Sierra. I bought it at an auction, with a loan from my mother after the fallout from my marital separation had left me penniless. It only had twenty thousand miles on the clock.

It was not until I'd handed over a thousand pounds to the impossibly dodgy auctioneer that I realised it had already been around the clock. I had also failed to notice that, in its previous life, the Sierra had seen service as a mini-cab. There were several incidents when stalled at traffic lights, the rear doors would open and a bevy of binge-drunk women or four fat blokes eating kebabs would pile in, demanding to be taken to a club.

"Why don't you get a proper car," my father would say, prodding one of the contusions in the top-of-the-range Citroen AZ I had acquired, with its fenestrations of algae and its amputated mirrors.

At last, very late in the day, I turned up at his house in an X-series Jaguar, its sleek contours and azure topcoat reeking of attainment. By this time he had become reconciled to a micro-habitat that was bounded by his upstairs bedroom, the adjacent bathroom, the stairs and the armchair that faced the TV. He had been officially designated too fragile to travel. But I had other ideas. Here was a proper car he could not resist.

I coaxed him out of the armchair and into the padded upholstery of the Jag, emphasising all its implausibly luxurious features as I strapped him in. We drove to Liverpool, our spiritual homeland, in silence, punctuated by the whisper of the effortlessly efficient two-and-a-half litre engine. We stopped at Crosby Beach. Here, one hundred bronze figures, cast by the sculptor Antony Gormally in the dimensions of his own body, gaze out to sea, towards America and the West Indies—routes that my father had traced in his younger days. We sat in the Jaguar in dazzling sunlight and listened to Mozart on the car's stereo.

Then there were the accommodations. These comprised the bulk of our verbal encounters. Mostly they involved sports and more likely Liverpool FC. A typical conversation would go something like this.

"Ian Rush is going to get a lot of goals for us this season."

"Yeah?"

Sport, football and Liverpool FC were de-militarised zones where we could talk about things that were neutral and neutered. In these safe spaces, we could disagree vehemently about whether Graham Souness was a dick-head without ever really disagreeing. It was a bit like shadow-boxing. It looked vicious, but no real blows were landed.

These spaces were highly efficient mechanisms for the propagation of stuckness. They created opportunities for diversions that enabled us to avoid asking uncomfortable questions about who we were and how our relationship was affecting our lives. Ian Rush became a key transitional subject in our psycho-theatre.

Just like in real life, the transitional Ian Rush was over-used. We played him far too often, instead of adopting the kind of careful rotation that characterised future team selection policy. And just like in real life, he ended up tired and increasingly ineffectual.

Ironically, sport was the catalyst for the only time I attempted to kindle a wholehearted dialogue with my father about my version of our shared history. Our stuckness. I took him on a golfing tour in Scotland. Neither of us could play golf.

On the one occasion I had tried swinging a club, on the championship course at Carnoustie, I'd ended up hitting the mud scraper. The ball had ricocheted backwards, landing some twenty feet to the rear of the tee. At least I had set foot on a golf course. In contrast, my father was a passive golfer. Apart from the boxing, he excelled at all sports that involved sedentary participation. From an armchair in front of the TV, he would take countless corners; smash scores of volleys and pot endless blacks without ever moving a muscle.

He was based in Dundee at the time of our golf tour, doing some testing on a new type of submersible for the off-shore oil rigs. We ended up in a bar on the outskirts of St Andrews—the Mecca of golf. It was probably the effects of four pints of heavy with malt chasers, but he suddenly turned round to me and said:

"I wasn't a bad father, was I?"

Here was the opportunity of a lifetime. An open invitation to let fly with all the psychic ammunition I'd stored up. But there they were again, the Holy Trinity—choice; procrastination and stuckness—standing together at the bar counter; raising their glasses and grinning. I felt that familiar weakening of resolve. Stuckness was winning. Better to let things lie. Better, surely, to pat him on the back and reassure him. Then I felt a flash of resentment as if I'd suddenly stepped out into a blazing sun. He wasn't getting away with this one. He had to be confronted.

I projectiled two decades of angst and resentment straight at him. The time when my mother had held me in her arms, like a shield, against his bunched fists. The time he'd come downstairs early one Christmas morning and belted us all for making too much noise. The time he'd left me—aged ten—on my own in a milk bar in Liverpool while he went next door for a pint. The absence of a birthday card on every birthday I could remember. Out it all poured. He took the onslaught without a word and without reaction.

When I had finally finished, he turned, looked me in the eye and said, "What are you having? It's my round."

But here, in this sale d'attente for the dying, whatever I'd been looking for in a small bar in St Andrews—blame; admission; contrition—didn't seem to matter anymore. Maybe I'd come looking for a miracle—the spirit of Lourdes in a dingy side ward in woolly-back land. Maybe I was hoping this was a momentary blip in my father's life.

After a few days on the ward, he would be packed off home, back to TV sports and DVDs of the Onedin Line. We'd take up where we left off and carry on as normal. I'd turn up from time to time, in the Jag and we would continue sparring, circling around the ring, neither of us willing or able, to land the knockout punch.

The knockout punch always comes when you least expect it. And it's always from an assassin waiting in the shadows. My dad was a cunt. But he was a beguiling cunt. A lovable cunt. A cunt that made you desperately want him to turn back the instant he turned away from the house, closed the gate and skipped down the road, with that jaunty seafarer's step. As if he was just popping into the Admiral Benbow for lunch.

Epilogue

The band called **Oasis** went on to produce thirteen albums, twenty-eight singles and thirty-six music videos. They sold 75 million records worldwide and were cited by Guinness World Records as the most successful act in the UK between 1995 and 2005.

I came across the scent of **Tiger Lillies** many years later in a taxi from Thessaloniki airport to the city centre, en route to a conference on developing competence frameworks for twenty-first-century skills. Along the way, the road was punctuated with posters advertising the band's forthcoming triumphal return to Thessaloniki Concert Hall.

Time Out once described them as imagine Kurt Weill conjuring up images of pre-war Berlin while a falsetto vocalist screams, squeaks and squawks his way through every number like some rambling madman and you've got the picture. They've been going for thirty years, released forty-five albums, took part in twenty-eight shows and appeared in nine films. They've had a Grammy nomination and won two Oliviers.

Flimsy went solo and does covers at weddings and corporate bashes.

The Manager married an electrician from Rickmansworth who she met on a dating site.

Mangal II is still Mangal II but it's turned into a high-end eatery that bears no resemblance to its former kebab glory days. The sons of the owner took advantage of the first COVID lockdown to take over from their dad, gut the whole place, install a suite of stainless steel kitchen cabinets and replace the indigenous staff with very polite English waiters.

Son the Younger applied the skills he'd picked up on a sabbatical to a Nordic Michelin three-star to radicalise the menu. You can still get a doner but it'll set you back over twenty quid. That's the only kebab they serve. Last time I was in, there was a whole brill on offer at forty quid a shot. You can't bring your own booze any more. The wines are curated to match the food items. There are no Turkish wines on the list.

Gilbert and George have defected to the arch-rivals around the corner—Mangal I—which now proudly displays a signed copy of one of their photo-art pieces. Switching to high-end was a stroke of genius. Mangal II is permanently packed and no-one is off their face on Casillero del Diablo.

The **Red Art** closed down, lay vacant for two years and has recently opened as a Turkish patisserie.

When it was safe, **Max** went back to West Africa. His family managed to reclaim most of the property stolen from it in the coup. He's now managing a hotel on a beach.

Cyrus does session gigs for famous musicians. He occasionally releases his own material on Soundcloud. He still lives in East Finchley.

Luddy Samms moved back to his birthplace—Negril, Jamaica and opened a club called 'The Drifters Bar and Entertainment Venue' where he performs and promotes "the best of International Entertainment for the delight of both the residents and the tourists."

Duff is a partner in a leading real estate consultancy. He has four kids and lives in Thames Ditton. **Brendan** married then divorced a Surinamese model. He shifts money around the world from an office in Canary Wharf. Duff and Brendan tour the London C-circuit in a covers band, playing anything and everything.

In 2013, **Hope Street** was voted the best street in the UK and Ireland by the Academy of Urbanism.

Father O'Dirty—real name Father John Murphy—was arrested, tried and sentenced two years ago for sexual offences involving minors. Now in his 90s, he's currently serving a twenty-year stretch in one of Her Majesty's hotels.

The **Trolley Stop** went up for sale. I was asked to join a consortium with the aim of buying it to keep it running as a music venue. I didn't have the cash. Shortly afterwards it was sold to a development company. It now accommodates expensive apartments.

Following a series of scandals, economic mismanagement and increasing public tedium with a Tory government that seemed to be going on forever, **New Labour,** under the stewardship of what was billed as a young, charismatic and electable leader, was heading into a General Election with a mixture of hope and the usual enduring pessimism. I wrote a new song in support called *Promises*. Here's the lyrics.

This place, this time, the face
showing no emotion
one look, one crime, the hook line
that we fell for
Promises are made to be broken
I've seen the truth of all your lies
promises are meant to be broken
look behind the headlines
open up your eyes
One dream, one creed, one nation
standing together
It's here, it's now, it's plain
that we've been seduced by
promises made to be broken
I've seen the truth of all your lies
Promises are meant to be broken
Look behind the headlines
open up your eyes
I know it's only dreaming
but why are we still stringing along
they'll trip you with their scheming
and it won't be long before you're singing their song
This place, this time, this prison
that you helped build
your move, your game, your chance
to turn the tables
Promises are made to be broken
I've seen the truth of all your lies
Promises are meant to be broken
Look behind the headlines
open up your eyes

I taped it on a four track, put the tape it in a Jiffy Bag and mailed it to **Peter Mandelson** at Labour HQ. The quality wasn't great but the song had a gripping hook line and a chorus that resonated with the zeitgeist and I felt sure they'd get back to me pretty quickly with a plan to incorporate it into their election campaign. I'd already worked out in my head the band we'd recruit to deliver the message to the masses.

On paper, its anthemic quality was made for Oasis. I could picture it being sung to an adoring mass of pissed-up left-leaning pimple-poppers as they waved their lighters in unison in front of the Glastonbury main stage. But Oasis were a bunch of Manc woolly-backs who'd stolen our opportunity for fame when they appeared on the undercard at the Water Rats in Kings Cross instead of us.

A more deserving vehicle to carry the torch was their arch-rival—Blur. The intricacy of language, the subtlety of the half-rhymes married at the same time to the populist refrain of the chorus cried out for Blur. They—and the song— ticked all the boxes that New Labour aspired to—cheeky but serious, Cockney but quintessentially middle-class. But in the end, I plumped for *Pulp*. Jarvis Cocker—ex-fish-seller, Leonard Cohen acolyte and Spiderman impressionist whose Sheffield roots would anchor the song in authentic proletarian soil.

I waited confidently for the Call. But, inexplicably, it never came. Six months later, Tony Blair engineered the biggest election landslide since the second world war. I cling to the unshakeable belief that *Promises* played an unacknowledged part in that victory, that Mandelson, like every good A&R man, played the tape at every strategy meeting in the run-up to the election to galvanise the troops. Nos quoque servimus qui soli stamus et exspectamus.